The Radar Army

The Radar Army

Winning the War of the Airwaves

REG BATT

ROBERT HALE · LONDON

ISBN 0 7090 4508 5

Robert Hale Limited
Clerkenwell House
Clerkenwell Green
London EC1R 0HT

Photoset in Palatino by
Derek Doyle & Associates, Mold, Clwyd.
Printed in Great Britain by
St Edmundsbury Press Limited, Bury St Edmunds, Suffolk.
Bound by WBC Bookbinders Ltd, Bridgend, Glamorgan.

Contents

*To those remarkable men of science with
whom it was a privilege to work*

Illustrations

Between pages 80 and 81

PICTURE CREDITS

The Royal Society: 1. The Clarendon Laboratory, Oxford: 2. Birmingham University, Department of Physics: 3. The Dee family collection: 4. Crown Copyright: 5, 6, 13, 16, 19, 20, 22, 23. Strathclyde University Archives: 7. Mrs Elaine Wheatley: 8. A.G.B. Lovell: 9. W.E. Burcham: 10. The Science Museum: 12. A.L. Hodgkin: 17. Malvern College Archive: 24, 25.

Foreword

On 21 February 1940 two young scientists, John Randall and Harry Boot, working under conditions of great secrecy in a laboratory of the Department of Physics at Birmingham University, gave birth to a remarkable invention – the cavity magnetron.

This fact may be quite meaningless to you the reader; it has possibly left you cold, but largely unknown to the general public this invention proved to be of earth-shattering proportions. Few have not been served by it nor witnessed it performing, for if in the past forty years you have made a journey by sea or air, then your safe and scheduled arrival would have been thanks largely to the cavity magnetron. If your kitchen is equipped with a microwave oven, then the heat to cook your meal will be generated by a cavity magnetron. If you have marvelled at man's achievements in space, the guidance and communications will most likely have been made using a cavity magnetron.

This book is not just the story of the magnetron however, nor specifically about Randall and Boot. It is about that which caused the magnetron to be invented and the contribution it made to winning the war. In short, it is the story of centimetre radar and of the remarkable men with whom I was privileged to work and who achieved what at the outset was regarded as impossible. It is mainly a story of people and places, of men rather than machines, though in the course of my narrative I do explain what makes the various items of microwave hardware tick. I trust, however, that those familiar with the technicalities of the subject will forgive me for explaining these things in

9

everyday language, eschewing formal scientific expressions likely to baffle 'the man on the Clapham omnibus'. In short, I have endeavoured to entertain both technical and non-technical readers, young and old.

Now why 10 centimetres, when such a short wavelength was well beyond the known technology of the day? Quite early in the development of the coastal radar chain which was to play a vital part in the Battle of Britain, it was realized that in the event of the enemy bombers being successfully located and repulsed in daylight, they were likely to resort to night bombing. In this case, each night-fighter would require its own radar on board to give it the equivalent of night vision.

In 1936 this seemed an impossibility. Nevertheless, a team at Bawdsey, Suffolk, under E.G. Bowen took on the task of developing compact systems operating on 1½ metres that could therefore be carried in aircraft. By the time war came, airborne systems both for locating ships at sea and for night-fighters had been developed. For the night-fighter application however, it was discovered that to be fully effective the serial system should produce a narrow beam, and the only way of achieving this in the space available on an aircraft was to use an even shorter wavelength – 10 centimetres or less.

Even though the prospect of a night-bombing campaign was regarded with great concern, those in authority had little faith that a centimetre system could be developed in a reasonable time – if indeed before the war had ended – neither did they think that scarce resources of trained manpower and material should be expended on such a scientific will-o'-the-wisp. It was hence with a degree of reluctance that the Telecommunications Research Establishment accepted the wild project. Possibly because they had no professional experience of radio, the task was passed on to some university researchers, but their unique ability to approach any job from first principles together with the fact that they were not shackled by knowledge of conventional radio techniques were the very ingredients that bred success.

This, therefore, is the starting point of my story: one of

adventure, excitement, frustration, administrative inertia, and even one of comedy. It is also a story of success. Before the war had ended, centimetre radar had become an indispensable ingredient of victory, not only in the air, but on land and sea as well. And in this day and age when it is fashionable to sell ourselves short, what is reported within these pages was a great British achievement.

My account is of events as I witnessed and have remembered them. Anecdotal in style, it is deliberately subjective in order to give readers a feel of the times. Relying upon one's memory can be hazardous, and information upon which we acted or reacted at the time could have been hearsay or even rumour, but official statements and records particularly in wartime can be subject to 'adjustment' for purposes of security, propaganda or just inter-departmental politics. Which therefore is the most reliable source? However, I can say that having met or corresponded with several of the personalities who participated in these events we are all in broad agreement as to the course of these affairs.

Persons mentioned have been addressed as they were at the time in question, and likewise serving officers have been given their rank, trusting that I have neither promoted nor demoted anyone unwittingly.

Units of measurement are in general those common at the time, for example some quantities are imperial rather than metric. Radio emissions are given in terms of wavelength not in frequency as is now the norm, but I have been unable to revert to the term 'cycles' which was used before 'herz' was adopted internationally.

There is much to relate and so it is with regret that my story must necessarily confine itself to the principal people involved. My apologies, therefore, to many erstwhile colleagues who have not been found a place in this saga.

I am most grateful to many people and organizations for their help in obtaining historic photographs. These include Miss Janet Dudley of RSRE Malvern, Mr Norman Rosser of Malvern College (rtd) and my son Graham of Graham Batt Fotodesign, Dusseldorf. Additionally I am indebted to Prof.

W.E. Burcham and Mr J.R. Atkinson, both of whom have kindly
provided some significant dates and valuable reminiscent gems
as well as photographs.

Finally, I wish to express my gratitude to my wife Dorothy,
not only for typing copious pages of manuscript but for patiently
correcting my spelling of which my English master frequently
despaired!

R.G.P. Batt,
Dorset, 1990

1   The Gathering of a Secret Army

It was Tuesday 14 May 1940, the day following the Whitsun Bank Holiday, which would prove to be the last such holiday observed until the war's end.

I was comfortably seated in a Southern express train which was speeding through the lush green Hampshire countryside *en route* for the little seaside town of Swanage, Dorset, where I was to join the Air Ministry Research Establishment at nearby Worth Matravers. I had been reflecting upon the events of the past many months and wondering what the future would bring.

It was now the ninth month of the Second World War. How different to expectations: instead of a holocaust it had largely been stalemate – the 'phony war,' they called it. Then came the spring, when no sooner had Prime Minister Neville Chamberlain made the remark 'Hitler has missed the bus' than the Führer, to everyone's surprise, launched invasions of Denmark and Norway in rapid succession.

The subjugation of Norway had been made easy by the fact that the Norwegian Prime Minister Quisling revealed himself as a collaborator, thereby adding a new word for traitor to the English language. The British response was an ill-planned and wholly inadequate landing by an expeditionary force on the inhospitable Norwegian coast, and by May failure was becoming evident. A government crisis ensued, and as the result of a vote of no confidence passed in the House, Winston Churchill became Prime Minister on 10 May – just four days before my journey.

* * *

I was one of about a dozen junior scientific assistants who had been recruited to the establishment at that time as part of a general expansion. This was afforded by the construction of a purpose-built site on the lonely, windswept St Alban's Head some four miles out of Swanage where it was supposed that work could proceed unhindered (and maybe unnoticed) by the enemy, which might not be the case were the establishment to remain at its original venue on the Suffolk coast.

There had been a degree of mystery about the whole thing since the Air Ministry had advertised the posts in the 'small ads' columns of the daily press, eschewing the normal, if pompous, 'Official Appointments' format. Interviews were held at Adastral House, Kingsway, then the headquarters of the ministry, but when the successful candidates were told to sit tight (like a theatrical agent saying 'We'll phone you') and that the ministry would negotiate our release from our various employers (I was with the Post Office Engineering Department) and any obligation for military service, the business took on a distinctly cloak-and-dagger air.

After arriving at Swanage and taking to the bus, which ground its way up the long hill through Langton Matravers to embrace the wild, rugged headland, we finally reached what had hitherto been the tranquil, ancient village of Worth Matravers. Just beyond and largely out of view of the village itself was an amazing scene of industrial activity made evident by the sight and sound of building workers busy with diggers, concrete mixers and hoists. The whole place was alive, like an anthill recently disturbed.

The small party joining that day, having reported to the guard-hut, was duly conducted to the administration block where from behind his desk in an office marked 'Civil Assistant and Accountant' the benign figure of the gentleman who had chaired the interview panel at Adastral House welcomed us.

This was Mr A.B. Jones, who was head of administration at AMRE. His had been an onerous task and was to continue to be so for the rest of his career. Over and above responsibility for personnel, pay, stores accounts and site services such as transport, cleaning, and so on, each time the establishment moved he would be subjected to a nightmarish burden, and there would be many departmental moves for him to oversee before he reached retirement well after the war.

We were beckoned to take seats after which Jones commenced by accounting for the delay since our interviews, necessarily incurred by our being vetted by MI5 for secret work. 'I can now tell you,' he continued, 'that the object of this establishment is the location of enemy aircraft using radio waves.' At this, someone in our party emitted an audible whistle which appropriately expressed how we all felt.

Following preliminary work, first at Slough in the spring of 1935 and then at Orford Ness, research was by 1936 well underway at Bawdsey Manor, which like Orford Ness was situated on the Suffolk coast. By the outbreak of the war, Britain was protected by a chain of coastal stations (designated CH) stretching from Scotland in the north to Ventnor on the Isle of Wight in the south. But for this radio tracking system, the Battle of Britain could never have been won by the RAF.

Britain was the first nation to be protected by such a system, then known to those in the secret as RDF, the code letters standing for Range and Direction Finding. The American term 'Radar' was adopted in Britain later in the war, replacing the unwieldy word 'Radiolocation' dreamt up by PR men when the government in July 1941 decided to disclose partially the existence of RDF. It was typical of the Americans that they should coin the more snappy word which was to stick and ultimately gain worldwide acceptance.

Our next port of call was the office of the assistant superintendent, Dr W.B. Lewis and his PA, Derrick Garrard, who were to acquaint us with the mysteries of this new science.

Dr Lewis was a truly brilliant individual – and I would use the word 'brilliant' sparingly of anyone. He was a chubby, curly-haired bachelor of thirty-two ('married to his work' according to his family), with a calm, friendly disposition. His mental capacity was formidable. Throughout the war, whatever the demands of his own office, he would make regular visits to each group in turn, where he would discuss their particular problems as lucidly as if he was one of their number. Frequently it was he who would provide the solution.

The feasibility of RDF having been demonstrated by the Bawdsey team under Robert Watson-Watt, orders for the equipment for a chain of stations had been placed in great secrecy with industry. Metropolitan Vickers of Manchester were given the contract for the transmitters operating over the range 6 to 15 metres; these were novel in the respect that instead of producing a steady emission, a brief pulse of high power at regular intervals was required, since the basic principle of RDF was that between successive pulses radio energy reflected by a target could be detected by a suitable receiver.

A.C. Cossor of London, under their chief engineer L.H. Bedord, were given the job of developing and manufacturing the receivers. The circuit techniques were similar to those being used for the new high-definition television service launched by the BBC in 1936, though more complex and sophisticated, but the choice of Cossor was astute since they were then the country's largest manufacturer of cathode-ray tubes and these would be needed to display the locational information.

With the development of 1½ metre technology many more detection systems became feasible, among these being a variety of air and shipborne applications (AI and ASV) as well as fixed (CHL) and mobile ground systems such as gun-laying (GL). There was now much work to be done urgently to expand and perfect the use of RDF in all its forms. In consequence the Bawdsey brigade, arriving from their various places of dispersal, were being augmented by experienced researchers from industry, the universities and public bodies such as the BBC and the Post Office.

As fast as builders could complete the huts, people were moved in to set up laboratories, offices and workshops. It was like the production of a major Hollywood movie for which a star cast was being assembled together with the electronic equivalent of script writers, set designers, carpenters and the like.

Most of the groups were in need of assistants and so there was some measure of choice for us new arrivals. The Lewis/Garrard talk had briefly mentioned 10 centimetres. This had caught my imagination – here was a real challenge. I duly volunteered to join the centimetre group. Garrard shrugged his shoulders slightly and warned me that at the moment very little practical work was being done on 10 centimetres; it was mainly theoretical. I was not to know that at that time centimetres were not the flavour of the month with AMRE's senior management. The subject was regarded with horror or derision according to one's view. In fact someone in high places had been heard to say 'Centimetres are not for this war'. Nevertheless I persisted and was duly introduced to a tall, well-built Canadian by the name of A.G. Ward who gladly claimed me as his assistant since he was not at that moment relishing the job of constructing some test equipment with his own hands.

I followed him out of the building in the middle of the main site which as well as containing the administrative centre included the various services buildings such as the main workshops, drawing office, test room, main stores, etc. Most of the buildings were simple single-storey constructions similar to those provided at army camps or aerodromes to house servicemen.

'This is B site,' informed Ward. 'We are over in A site,' he added, pointing to a separate compound on the further side of a farm track. I found Ward's Canadian drawl quite fascinating as he explained to me that the centimetre group's hut was in the course of being built down on C site, which he vaguely indicated across some fields beyond. The group such as it existed was hence split up and camping out wherever space could be found in other groups' huts.

Immediately beyond the A site compound, looking as if it had been pushed back out of the way, was Renscombe Farm, which had suddenly found itself with a major industrial complex on its doorstep. A sizeable proportion of the farm's productive area had temporarily been relinquished when the Air Ministry had requisitioned some 120 acres at St Alban's Head. Right at the very tip of the headland was a small CHL site designated 'D'. It was perched on the very edge of the 200-foot high cliffs. Later a further site would be added across the road opposite the main gate. It would be graced by a 360-foot steel transmitter tower and would be known as E site. Within each of A and B sites stood a single 240-foot wooden tower as well as other lesser structures.

Until the centimetre group's hut was completed Ward was 'camping' in the Receiver Group hut, not inappropriate in a sense since Ward's contribution to the new art was to contrive a 10 centimetre receiver. 'We are at a standing start,' he declared, 'since there are no valves capable of working normally at such low wavelengths. Fifty centimetres just, but 10 centimetres definitely not.' He then went on to explain that this was due to an effect called transit time. This was the time taken for the electrons emitted by the filament of a thermionic valve to pass between the grid and anode electrodes. At these very high frequencies the electrons could not keep in step with an external oscillatory circuit. To some one like myself accustomed to working at broadcast frequencies, it was like being told that our motor cars were useless because they could not keep up with a bullet in full flight. Then there was the fact that the shortest piece of connecting wire was no longer just a piece of connecting wire but in itself a tuned circuit and one of embarrassing proportions.

The initial problem, notwithstanding these serious limitations, was to concoct some form of local oscillator – an essential ingredient to any sensitive receiver. The other problem was to find a suitable signal detector. 'But that's another question,' said Ward with a gentle smile – Ward always said things with a gentle smile. 'But what about a transmitter?' I enquired. 'We've got something for that,' he replied. 'It's called a klystron – it uses resonant cavities for tuned circuits – the Americans call them rhumbatrons.'

What kind of madhouse had I elected to join? Here was I, having recently acquired formal radio-engineering qualifications, encountering alien concepts such as transit time and resonant cavities – a far cry from broadcast communications.

It was now time for a tea break (an anathema to AMRE's superintendent, who considered young healthy individuals should be able to work without need of tea breaks – an expressed opinion which tended to popularize coffee!) and to meet two important members of the group: Dr H.W.B. Skinner and J.R. Atkinson. They greeted me with genuine warmth which somewhat took me aback, used as I was to a hierarchical institution such as the Post Office, where a junior grade would know his place. It seemed I had now entered the more democratic ambience of university researchers.

Dr Skinner from the Wills physical laboratory at Bristol University had been handed the job of leading a 10 centimetre group by a disinterested management earlier that year. Shortly afterwards he had been joined by Jimmy Atkinson, a Bawdsey man who had latterly been touring the CH stations on a special assignment. Upon his arrival, Skinner was to remark in his acknowledged brand of dry wit that Atkinson's coming had doubled the size of the team!

Theirs was a partnership which was to flourish throughout the war years. They were ideally complementary, for whereas Skinner was a quiet, thoughtful visionary, Atkinson was an ebullient and outgoing character. They were both accomplished experimenters and tireless workers. Neither stood on dignity whenever there was a job to be done in the lab.

Skinner, the senior by age and standing, enjoyed an acknowledged measure of respect in scientific circles, his observations and opinions invariably proving sound and valid. Jimmy Atkinson, with his head of dark curly hair, was endowed with limitless charm which was to be a great asset to the group. With his knowledge of the RAF stores system and the ways of management he could wheedle the most scarce of wartime commodities out of the hardest-hearted of administrators. He could muster willing help from any quarter, whether it be from workshops, transport, the constabulary or even the army and navy. Both men were inveterate pipe-smokers, and whether at work, car driving, or just in conversation, their pipes would be constantly lit and relit.

It would be at least a fortnight before I would encounter the top man at AMRE – Superintendent A.P. Rowe (popularly known as Jimmy Rowe for a quite obscure reason). He appeared in the lab one afternoon with a party of VIPs. Insignificant in stature, he had none of the visible attributes of a chief of a dynamic organization. But his forte was communication. To him it was a tool, an instrument to oil the wheels. Information was the primary ingredient of motivation, especially for researchers, followed by discussion and the interplay of ideas. This was his philosophy and *modus operandi.*

His stock-in-trade was the station order. These would appear with the regularity of latter-day opinion polls. They would inform, even stimulate new developments to solve the problems of war, but sometimes they would offend and even appear petty, such as on the occasion when one complaining of the unshaven appearance of some members of the staff proceeded to instruct us in the art of sharpening used razor blades on the inside of a tumbler.

The apotheosis of his philosophy, however, was without doubt his legendary Sunday Soviets. These were regular occasions when service chiefs and senior civil servants would be invited down to meet in Rowe's office for informal, no-holds-barred discussions with his senior staff. It was acknowledged by the visitors to be stimulating and refreshing to take the occasional Sunday off to travel out of town to exchange problems and ideas. The value derived from these meetings was immeasurable. Neither the enemy nor our American allies enjoyed such a unique and direct interplay of ideas between their armed services and civilian scientists.

It was possibly thanks to Rowe that Britain had RDF at all. It was in 1934 when he was assistant to H.E. Wimperis, the first director of scientific research at the Air Ministry, that he became aware of the problems of air defence. The methods then available involved location by sound detectors and defence by anti-aircraft gunnery. The increasing speed of military aircraft made these systems no longer feasible. Standing patrols of fighter aircraft were economically unacceptable on account of the large numbers required.

The rise of Hitler to absolute power in Germany brought a sense of great urgency to these problems. It therefore appeared advisable that help be sought from the best scientific brains of the day. Hence it was that a committee for the scientific survey of air defence was formed, of which Rowe was secretary. The chairman appointed was Sir Henry Tizard, who was at that time secretary of the Department of Scientific and Industrial Research (DSIR). It therefore became known as the 'Tizard Committee'. Included on this committee were Professor P.M.S. Blackett, A.V. Hill and H.E. Wimperis himself.

A notable absentee in the first instance was Professor F.A. Lindemann of Oxford's Clarendon Laboratory. Although a friend of Tizard, the fact that he had long been on close terms with Winston Churchill, then a back-bencher and leader of a rival faction, was sufficient reason for his exclusion. In due course he was admitted to the committee but this resulted in some stormy sessions as brilliant minds clashed over the efficacy of rival schemes. Nevertheless, the Tizard Committee were responsible for some important recommendations, the most vital being that of RDF itself.

This came about as an offshoot of a completely different idea – the possibility of the so called 'death ray'. To assess the feasibility of such a scheme Wimperis had sought the advice of Watson-Watt, superintendent of the radio department at the National Physical Laboratory. The question was, could a beam of radio waves be produced which would have sufficient power to damage an object such as an aircraft? That serious professional attention should have been applied to an idea then existing in science fiction pre-dates President Reagan's 'Star Wars' concept by fifty years.

Watson-Watt was able to show mathematically that although such a scheme was feasible in principle it was nevertheless completely out of scale with the degree of radio frequency power it was practical to generate and emit as a beam. He suggested, however, that a technique which had been developed by E.V. Appleton to measure the height of the ionized layers above the earth by bouncing radio waves off a reflective surface might be applied to receiving reflected energy from an object as small as an aircraft.

A legendary experiment was hence made on 26 February 1935 by A.F. Wilkins of Watson-Watt's staff. With a receiver fitted up in a van stationed at Weedon, close to the BBC's powerful Empire Short Wave transmitter at Daventry radiating on a wavelength of 49 metres, Wilkins successfully demonstrated that the amount of radio energy reflected by the surface of an aircraft flying within the field of radiation was sufficient to be detected by a suitable receiver. The aircraft used for the experiment was a Handley Page Heyford bomber from RAE Farnborough. As it flew a circuit within the area of the BBC's transmitter, the received signal displayed as a spot on a cathode-ray tube rose and fell as the reflected signal from the bomber successively added and subtracted itself from the otherwise steady signal level direct from the transmitter. This was the same beat effect noticeable on the older 405-line TV reception when an aircraft flew overhead.

Following the Wilkins experiment things moved fast and ten weeks later a group had been set up at Orford Ness on the Suffolk coast under the leadership of Watson-Watt who had been loaned to the Air Ministry by DSIR. In less than twelve months the group had outgrown its humble accommodation at Orford Ness and so Watson-Watt and Wilkins took it upon themselves to find something larger. They did not need to venture very far for they discovered Bawdsey Manor, twelve miles to the south near Felixstowe, and the owner, Sir Cuthbert Quilter, was persuaded to sell to the Air Ministry. A year following the start at Orford Ness, Bawdsey Research Station came into being.

Two years later, in May 1938, Watson-Watt was appointed Director of Communications Development (DCD) at the Air Ministry to oversee all RDF work, including the construction of the chain stations, and A.P. Rowe became Superintendent of the Bawdsey establishment, now known as AMRE. Four months later the alarm bells of war were sounding.

Now in May 1940 a significant expansion was taking place, putting the establishment on a firm war footing, and Rowe's staff were powerfully augmented by many of the country's top scientists and engineers, men of sharp intellect and independent mind. These sudden changes in the character of the establishment were to result in friction, not unwarranted, between Rowe and the newcomers. It seemed that being ingrained in Civil Service orthodoxy, he was ill equipped to lead a large experimental organization in wartime. His guiding principle was what the Germans refer to as *'Alles in Ordnung'* (everything in order – according to the rules). But war breeds chaos.

He never fully understood or appreciated academics, whose *laissez-faire* ways of working were not to his liking. A classic example was a station order stating that it had come to his notice that staff were variously arriving for work up to an hour after the appointed starting time. With this he completely ignored the fact that everyone worked through to 7 p.m. each day quite voluntarily, and frequently into the night. He had appended a note to the copy delivered to our group which Skinner read out to us all with some amusement. It said: 'and you Skinner are among the worst offenders'. It was quite absurd since few worked longer hours than Skinner. In his notice Rowe conceded that staff occasionally worked late, in which case he suggested there was then justification for coming in later – say 10 a.m. The result was that if one could not make it by eight one hung around Swanage until ten!

He was sometimes critical of people's attire, suggesting that a person should dress more suitably when VIPs were to arrive. On one such occasion Jimmy Atkinson was sent off to get his hair cut! In spite of such tribulations Rowe successfully welded this disparate army of individuals into an outstanding war-winning machine.

2   The Cavendish Connection

I was into my second week at AMRE, during which time I had been kept busy constructing equipment for Ward's centimetre receiver experiments, when we had a visit from two people who had just arrived on site to join the new group.

The elder of the two was a tall, gaunt-looking, schoolmasterly figure wearing gold-rimmed spectacles and bearing a remarkable resemblance to our senior Latin master at school. I made a mental note to keep out of his way. But that was my first impression, which turned out to be completely in error. In fact this gentleman, P.I. Dee, who was to be joint group leader with Dr Skinner, was a kind, fatherly person with a gentle sense of humour. There were to be callers who in ignorance or doubt would address him as Dr Dee or Professor Dee, not believing that a scientist of such repute could be just plain Mr Dee here at AMRE, where PhDs were thick on the ground. (A Swanage local had said to me: 'Haven't you got a lot of doctors up at Worth?' thinking they were all MDs). Once, when asked to explain this enigma, his reply – doubtless made with a smile – was that he had been far too occupied with conducting his researches to expend time on such formalities. After the war, however, he became Professor and head of the department of Natural Philosophy at Glasgow University, a Fellow of the Royal Society, and was awarded the CBE. Latter-day callers would have been much happier.

Dee's companion was Dr W.E. Burcham – Bill Burcham to his friends. A dedicated scientist, he had a friendly, unruffled manner which made working for him a pleasure. In the post-war years he was to become the Oliver Lodge Professor of Physics at Birmingham University and he too became a Fellow of the Royal Society and was awarded the CBE.

Both Dee and Burcham were part of the strong contingent from Cambridge University's famous Cavendish Laboratory. It was once suggested that 'The Cavendish brigade ran the Second World War, scientifically speaking.' As a factual statement this is a little exaggerated but the underlying sentiment is true enough. The Cavendish was indeed a special institution, long established and with an unrivalled history of achievement. Of all the country's technical and scientific institutions, the Cavendish undoubtedly made the greatest contribution to the scientific war effort in terms of the numbers and expertise of its people.

It was no accident that the Cavendish men were in the van of the forces of science and technology answering the call at the outbreak of the war. It was part of a plan by none less than Sir Henry Tizard when early in 1938 he invited John Cockcroft to lunch at the Athenaeum. Cockcroft at that time was second professor to Sir Lawrence Bragg, the Cavendish Professor and successor in that chair to the great Lord Rutherford.

Cockcroft was well chosen by Tizard, not merely on account of his seniority at the laboratory, but for his achievements in partnership with E.T.S. Walton, with whom he had succeeded in artificially accelerating atomic particles by means of high voltages. Cockcroft, who had been a college apprentice at the Metropolitan-Vickers electrical works before entering the Cavendish, was hence a very capable electrical engineer in his own right. With Walton he had devised and built the apparatus used in those experiments which produced the enormous voltage, for 1929, of 300,000.

Tizard appreciated that the new technology of RDF, which was then well in production following the Bawdsey developments, would need the help of a significant number of highly trained professionals if its introduction into service was to proceed smoothly and without undue delays. Hence the lunch at which Tizard confided the secrets of RDF to

Cockcroft, whilst asking whether such help could be available from the Cavendish should war break out.

Following this meeting contact was established with Watson-Watt at Bawdsey through which the senior staff of the Cavendish, including Dee, Lewis and Ratcliffe, were to be made acquainted with the details of RDF by the key people at Bawdsey, namely Bowen, Williams, Larnder, Whelpton and Wilkins.

In September of 1938, following A.P. Rowe's appointment as Superintendent at Bawdsey in succession to Watson-Watt, Dr Lewis was appointed as his deputy.

Hence it was that as hostilities were about to break out, the Cavendish men, together with colleagues from other universities, were well briefed and organized as a result of Cockcroft's efforts; they were ready to take to the field, and did so on 1 September 1939. At this time Cockcroft's team was no less than eighty strong.

Organized into a number of parties, they were dispersed around the various sites which were ranged all along the east and south coasts of Britain. Not only did they concern themselves with troubleshooting at the CH stations but became involved with construction when a corresponding chain of Coast Defence (CD) sets on 1½ metres was urgently required to detect enemy shipping, particularly mine-layers. These sets, by virtue of their shorter wavelength and rotatable beam aerials, were found to be useful in detecting low-flying aircraft and hence led to the creation of the CHL (Chain-Low) chain.

By the early months of 1940 the Air Ministry had set up a regular organization which assumed responsibility for this work. The university parties were thus able to return to their respective bases where they could take up the occupation for which they were trained, namely research.

Cockcroft himself returned to the War Department orbit where he had been appointed Assistant Director of Scientific Research. As such he took on a largely roving commission, since his abilities were constantly in demand in many quarters – such as his membership of the Tizard Commission to North America in the autumn of 1940. Throughout, however, he was closely connected with the Air Defence Research and Development Establishment (ADRDE), becoming Superintendent in April 1941. Whilst AMRE was at Worth Matravers our WD cousins of ADRDE were stationed at Christchurch, a mere thirty miles to the east along the coast.

ADRDE were principally concerned with the application of RDF to gunnery and in due course the army began to experience problems in providing adequate training to match the rate of introduction of new systems. J.A. Ratcliffe, whose abilities as a lecturer were outstanding, was borrowed from AMRE no sooner than he had returned from the field-work of 1939–40. A new army training centre was set up at Petersham in Surrey with Ratcliffe as its superintendent. Graduates and members of the teaching profession were recruited and trained as civilian radio officers to be sent out to the AA gunsites. Their function was not only to oversee the operation and maintenance of the GL (gun-laying) radars, but unofficially to act as 'salesmen' with the object of convincing disbelieving battery commanders that 'this new-fangled RDF stuff' could actually work.

With Petersham successfully functioning, Ratcliffe returned to AMRE during 1941, where he set up a similar organization to facilitate the introduction of new radar systems into service with the RAF. The Forres School building in Swanage was requisitioned for the purpose of accommodating the Ratcliffe organization. During the winter of 1941–42 a series of evening lectures was organized for the benefit of AMRE staff themselves. Some of the lectures were given by Ratcliffe himself and these were a joy to experience. I have always had the propensity to 'nod-off' during a lecture, whether I am interested in the subject or not. Those who have succeeded in holding my attention throughout the whole duration of their discourse are exceedingly few in number and of these J.A. Ratcliffe tops the list. Not only was he an interesting and entertaining speaker but he possessed that rare ability to make mundane and even uninteresting subjects lucid and exciting.

Many of the Cavendish people had before the war taken chairs at other universities, taking with them the ways and tradition of the Cavendish. P.M.S. Blackett had gone to Manchester and had been an important member of the Tizard Committee. In 1940 he was appointed Scientific Adviser to AA Command where he set up a group which applied statistical and analytical techniques to measure the effectiveness of anti-aircraft gunnery. He was later to apply the same methods at RAF Coastal Command, where he had the same position as Scientific Adviser to the AOC-in-C. The technique, now well established, was given the title 'Operational Research'. Blackett's group was a powerful one, having among its number no less than five Fellows of the Royal Society.

Also to make the transition from Cavendish to Manchester was B.V. Bowden, who in 1963 became Lord Bowden of Chesterfield when given a place in Harold Wilson's Labour government. In 1939 he was one of Cockcroft's 'troops', after which he settled in at AMRE, where he became responsible for IFF (Identification Friend or Foe) development. Later in the war he was to move to Washington, where he headed the British team in the combined research group set up to develop an Anglo-American version of IFF (the mark V); IFF was a wholly British invention and a vital ingredient of radar – it avoided the inherent danger of intercepting one's own aircraft.

The Australian Mark Oliphant had maintained the antipodean connection at the Cavendish initiated by Lord Rutherford, who was a New Zealander. He had taken a chair at Birmingham, where he went to continue nuclear research. The big-machine age of science had arrived and Oliphant and his team, including J.T. Randall and H.A.H. Boot, were involved with the construction of a cyclotron which was to be brought to a halt by the war. The Cavendish already had one of these large machines which uses a combination of a powerful electro-magnet and high-power short wave energy as an alternative method of accelerating atomic particles to that of the Cockcroft/Walton high-voltage system.

The Oliphant team left the comfort of their elegant red-brick university in Birmingham to join the 'Cockcroft army' in 1939. The party was despatched to Ventnor but after a few weeks, which were not greatly productive, they returned to Birmingham to take on the infinitely more important task of developing centimetre transmitter valves, a project for which they were well equipped.

Meanwhile, what of the two gentlemen who prompted this tale of the Cavendish? Dee, Burcham and their associates had been furthering the work of Cockcroft and Walton in the High Tension Laboratory or 'HT lab' for short. In 1936 the motor-car magnate Herbert Austin donated a quarter of a million pounds (about £8 million in today's money) to the university in recognition of Rutherford's work. Appropriately it was put to building and equipping an extension to the laboratory. The HT lab was part of this programme and here Dee and his team (with a little help from the Philips electrical firm) constructed what looked like a giant space-age monster. With this equipment they succeeded in generating voltages of the order of one million, no great deal in terms of 1980s big science but a record-breaking effort in the thirties.

Although Dee had been a member of Cockcroft's RDF survey team in the spring of 1939, when war broke out in September the Dee party were despatched to Exeter, where at an outstation of the Royal Aircraft Establishment Farnborough they went to work on a project designated PAC.

The letters stood for Parachute and Cable, a system intended for defending airfields against enemy air attack. A ring of barrage balloons would have been out of the question for obvious reasons, but with PAC the same effect could be had at the press of a button at the time of an enemy approach. A line of cables would be shot into the air by rockets (in the same manner as the breeches buoy in maritime rescue) where they would remain in suspension for a short while on parachutes.

To Rowe this was just another hair-brained scheme in the same category as a pet scheme of Professor Lindemann's, which proposed the use of aerial mines suspended from airborne cables. That Lindemann with a certain amount of support from

Churchill persisted in pushing this scheme led to much hostility within the Tizard Committee. And so it was when Dee and Burcham eventually arrived at Worth Matravers on 15 May 1940, Rowe was positively scathing about what he regarded as six wasted months which (in his view) could have been better employed at AMRE.

It was therefore most ironic that a few months later a line of PACs was installed by the RAF between B and C sites. There was one occasion when the array was fired in anger – as it happened by mistake. Luckily for the surprised crew of the RAF Blenheim, even though they had been flying low the cables did not quite make the height.

So, when Dee and Burcham finally arrived at Worth Matravers ready to help tackle the 10 centimetre problem, there would have been a common bond since Skinner himself had been at the Cavendish between 1922 and 1927.

3   Dunkirk and the Fall of France

Ward's efforts to devise a local oscillator for the projected 10 centimetre receiver were concentrated upon a unique principle due to Barkhausen and Kurz.[1] Whether any particular valve could operate in the B – K mode depended as much on the proportions of the electrode assembly as on the external parameters. Hence it was that I had been busy testing each of a collection of unusual triode valves which Ward had acquired. So far the results had been disappointing for we had not found one to oscillate at any wavelength lower than 80 centimetres.

We were well into this fruitless pursuit when, arriving at the receiver group hut one morning, we were confronted by a motley collection of mobile RDF trailers, diesel-electric generators and heavy touring vehicles which had mysteriously arrived during the night and were now crowded into a corner of B site compound. Their air of frantic abandon left no doubt in our minds that something was afoot. We were to learn that these mobile sets had been providing local RDF cover at forward airfields in France but now they had been hastily withdrawn via Calais. Two days later the evacuation of Dunkirk had begun.

By this remarkable operation, which spanned nine violent days between 27 May and 4 June, around 300,000 British troops were rescued from the onslaught of the German Panzers which, by-passing the vaunted Maginot Line and sweeping across the Lowlands, took everyone by surprise. By 14 June Paris had fallen to be followed by complete capitulation by France on the 17th. Britain was now alone, with the enemy massed along the Normandy coast, and when Churchill made the first of his memorable speeches on the radio – 'We shall fight on the beaches, we shall fight in the fields and in the streets, we shall fight in the hills, we shall never surrender' – it struck a chord with us: we were in the front line. We lined up to join the Local Defence Volunteers (LDV) – later to be renamed the Home Guard – but for logistical reasons it would be some time before AMRE had its own squad.

Now France had capitulated it seemed certain that our turn to face the enemy would soon come. We were not surprised therefore when Churchill made his second broadcast in which he warned the country of the fleets of barges then being assembled at all the captured Channel ports from Rotterdam to Le Havre, together with a whole variety of naval craft which had been observed by RAF reconnaissance flights. Hitler's invasion plan – Operation Sealion – was now underway.

With a 'backs to the wall' spirit Britain prepared as best she could to resist the anticipated onslaught. Resources were gravely depleted but the British flair for improvisation well compensated for any lack of equipment and material. Everywhere gangs of soldiers and civilian workers could be seen with concrete mixers hastily constructing tank traps, pill boxes and gun emplacements at strategic points such as road junctions, bridges, and at approaches to towns and villages; many remain to this day.

The whole of the south coast to a depth of twenty miles was declared a Defence Area within which no one other than local residents, members of the armed forces and authorized workers such as ourselves could travel or reside. But for the presence of AMRE this could have spelt disaster for Swanage. Fortuitously the establishment had brought a bonanza – it was as if there was a never-ending holiday season with guest houses, hotels and what furnished and unfurnished accommodation was available, all bursting at the seams.

It was at this time that one of Rowe's station orders was circulated. This one was urgent and was passed around from hand to hand. If any of these notices had from time to time been treated with disdain, this was one to be taken in all seriousness. It spelt out the parlous war situation Britain was now facing.

Expressed in detail which could only have come down to him from Whitehall, it was a most effective way of convincing all Rowe's scientific staff that their efforts must be redoubled. Leave, which had already been restricted, was now suspended until further notice and a six-day working week introduced. Far from these measures being resented, most took to working each day until 7 p.m. which became the norm throughout the war.

During the last full weekend before the new regimen I had slipped home to London to fetch some more clothing but more importantly to collect my bicycle. I was now fully mobile and would make the steady climb up through Langton Matravers each day to work, no longer having to worry about stopping work in time to catch the bus back to my lodgings. Little was I then aware that in its humble way my machine was destined to make history.

Footnote

1. The Barkhausen–Kurz oscillator uses a triode valve with which the grid electrode is given a positive potential while the anode is made zero or slightly negative. The electrons emitted from the filament are hence accelerated towards the grid where a proportion of them will shoot through. Upon reaching the anode region they are repelled by its relative negative potential and as a result they will be attracted back to the grid. By critically adjusting the grid potential, the rate of the to and fro movement of the electrons can be made coincident with that in an external tuned circuit (generally consisting of a length of transmission line) connected between grid and anode. At any given frequency the geometry of the valve's electrode structure is important, that having a cylindrical anode being desirable.

4 The Battle of the Beams

We were into the third week of June when late one afternoon telephones in group leaders' offices around the establishment were ringing urgently. The message was that nobody was to leave the site until further notice.

What was afoot? Much speculative conversation broke out among colleagues.

With no explanation nor clue a message came an hour after normal leaving time that we were now at liberty to go home.

The next day we learnt via the grapevine that the men who had been seconded from the radio section of the Post Office engineering department had been rounded up and promptly despatched that evening in an official car in the direction of London.

It was some weeks before we knew the purpose of their urgent departure. In one word, '*Knikebeine*'. This was the code word for a German radio navigation system which enabled the Luftwaffe's night bombers to locate selected targets over England. For several months, Dr R.V. Jones, who headed the Scientific Intelligence Unit at the Air Ministry, had been methodically piecing together a varied selection of information and now he was convinced he knew how the system operated; more disturbing was the knowledge that it was already in use.

Jones's report to the RAF command reached the War Cabinet to which he was summoned for a meeting by Churchill himself. Whenever matters came into the Prime Minister's orbit people were made to jump, and this occasion was no exception. Various ideas were advanced – 'jam them'; 'bend the beams'. However, before countermeasures could be devised it was essential to obtain fairly precise details of the system.

It was arranged that a special unit of the RAF which had experience of radio-beam navigation would attempt the tricky and dangerous job of flying back down the German beams, whilst ground monitoring of the enemy transmissions was to be carried out from selected sites on the east coast. Those best equipped for the latter task were our Post Office colleagues, who from their work in the radio section had experience in tracing unauthorized transmissions.

Several months elapsed before we saw them back on site during which time some countermeasures had been devised which were not without success. However, these had to be applied with due circumspection in order not to betray the fact that Britain was in possession of a German Enigma code machine with which intercepted messages could be decoded. This was being used to obtain information on the beam bearings for selected targets.

Appreciation of the value to the enemy of such a navigational system led our own scientists to devise equivalents. The first of these was GEE conceived by R.J. Dippy, one of the Bawdsey originals. It had a number of advantages over the German continuous-wave radio system, for it employed a radar-type pulse system which was not as easy to jam. Also it enabled an aircraft to determine its position at any time by reference to measured time differences of the synchronized pulses from three widely spaced stations, whereas *Knikebeine* was a single-point system directing bombers to one selected target. A crash programme of production was put in hand during the winter of 1941–2 with Dynatron Radio of Maidenhead, who before the war specialized in high-class custom-built radios. The first successful use of the device was in a raid on the Baltic port of Lübeck in March 1942, and from that time onwards Germany would no longer treat the efforts of Bomber Command with derision.

Another system that was to be developed was the brainchild of A.H. Reeves, who had been seconded from the research laboratories of Standard Telephones and Cables; it was called Oboe. Early experiments involved the transmission of an audible tone which one of the experimenters thought sounded like an oboe. Although the system in its ultimate form bore little resemblance to that of the early trials, what had originally caught on as a nickname became the official code word.

The idea when originally proposed met with hostility in high places and was in danger of never getting off the ground (literally). However, in the capable hands of Dr F.E. Jones it was proved to be feasible and thrived to the extent that it became the most accurate of any of the wartime blind-bombing systems.

Like GEE it made use of accurate time (i.e. distance) measurements from two widely spaced and synchronized pulse transmitters, but whereas GEE enabled the navigators in any number of aircraft simultaneously to pinpoint their positions using a combination of the time measurements and a specially prepared chart, with Oboe the radar measurements and hence the control was carried out by a ground controller. This meant that in effect only one bomber at a time could be dealt with and it would have to fly precisely and steadily upon the arc of its course over the target area for a duration of approximately ten minutes in making its drop.

Under such circumstances an aircraft would be particularly vulnerable to interception or attack from AA guns. Furthermore it would appear easy to jam the transmission, and at a rate of ten minutes per drop the bombing rate would be much too low. These were the criticisms which nearly ditched the project. But then a series of changes in the circumstances occurred which placed the whole idea in a new light.

First came the idea of the 'pathfinder,' a single aircraft equipped to locate a given target over which it would drop a target-indicating flare. Following would be the main bomber force which would unload its bombs, high-explosive or incendiary, over the area marked by the flare. This removed the objection of a low bombing rate.

Secondly, and most significant, was the development of the de Havilland Mosquito. This was the most beautiful of any wartime aircraft. It was a medium-size multi-role aircraft of outstanding performance in speed, height, and manoeuvrability. Such an aircraft could well look after itself should it be intercepted when on a pathfinder mission.

Finally, it was demonstrated that the characteristics of the transmitted signals were such that enemy jamming did not prove to be a problem.

Oboe as developed under the leadership of Dr F.E. Jones became a potent weapon in the hands of Bomber Command. It was particularly successful in targeting the raids over the Ruhr and ultimately was to have a vital task to perform in the build-up towards the invasion of Europe.

* * *

During the summer the establishment found itself under a new master. Whereas the composition of the Chamberlain government was hardly changed at the outbreak of the war, when Winston Churchill came to power he lost no time in creating an entirely new team. In the first place he chose to make it a coalition government to ensure the co-operation of the opposition, but this also enabled him to select the best talent from all the parties. From the upper house he drew a number of experts such as Lord Woolton whom he made Minister of Food, but first and foremost he called on an old friend, Lord Beaverbrook, the dynamic Canadian proprietor of Express Newspapers.

As a result of his own experience of a Ministry of Munitions in the First World War Churchill took the view that the Air Ministry should devote its energies to fighting the war and that a separate ministry should have the job of providing the hardware. Hence it was that the Ministry of Aircraft Production was born and who better to run it, he considered, than that human dynamo Lord Beaverbrook.

A similar provision was made in respect of the War Department with the creation of the Ministry of Supply. Strangely (or perhaps typically) the Admiralty was left to its own devices but doubtless the Ministry of Supply was responsible for the provision to all three services of such common items of equipment as ammunition and toilet rolls.

Finding ourselves transferred from the Air Ministry to Aircraft Production we were no longer AMRE but MAPRE. What horror! 'What's in a name?' the saying goes but whereas 'AMRE' rolled easily off the tongue, MAPRE, particularly when attempted at speed over the telephone, was a different matter.

Fortunately, within about a month some minion tucked away in the darkest recesses of Whitehall came up with a much better title for us – 'Telecommunications Research Establishment.' This had a twin advantage: (a) since our work was nothing to do with telecommunications it would, we hoped, fool the enemy, and (b) the initial letters TRE flowed easily from the tongue.

After the war the establishment received Crown recognition and became known as the Royal Radar Establishment, and then in the early 1970s as an economy measure the Signals Research and Development Establishment, hitherto at Christchurch, was integrated with RRE. Hence it is now the Royal Signals and Radar Establishment (RSRE – Malvern). A long march from the days of the Bawdsey Research Station.

5   An Infernal Machine

By the middle of June 1940 the hut at C site which had been allocated to our 10 centimetre group was completed by the builders and ready to be occupied. As soon as Ward and I had completed a particular set of measurements we collected our equipment together ready for transport to our new home.

Ward and I were not the first arrivals, for Skinner, Dee, Burcham and Atkinson had already installed themselves. So too had some new faces, principal among them being Dr Lovell (now Sir Bernard Lovell of Jodrell Bank fame) from Manchester University together with Chapman, his own lab assistant at the university, and also some precious items of workshop equipment borrowed for the duration.

Lovell came to AMRE as a member of 'Cockcroft's army' and was attached to Dr E.G. Bowen, one of the original Bawdsey team who was pioneering airborne RDF systems. While the bulk of the Bawdsey staff were evacuated to Dundee, the airborne RDF group were initially sent to Perth airfield and later transferred to RAF St Athan in Wales. With this group Bowen Lovell worked on 1½ metre AI (Airborne Interception), hence he came to the 10 centimetre group with valuable experience of airborne equipment in general and of AI in particular.

Having unloaded our equipment and carried it into the new hut I had a chance to look around. It was mid-morning and we were just in time to join Dr Skinner for a cup of tea. In the days that followed I was to discover that Skinner was the principal tea-maker. He had organized the equipment which included an

39

old brown china teapot with a saucer in place of its missing lid, and it was he who brought in the tea and milk.

As we sipped our tea (I seem to remember sitting on a packing case to do so) Ward and Skinner were in conversation regarding the state of the art of our work. Here it was that Skinner made the fantastic pronouncement that it was 1 centimetre rather than 10 centimetres which was the real problem for the establishment. He went on to suggest that if we couldn't find a valve capable of performing as a detector at these wavelengths we would have to fall back on the use of a crystal detector. Crystal detectors, complete with cat's whisker – fundamentally no different from my father's 1924 wireless set for listening-in to 2LO! This really is a madhouse, I reflected.

The feeling was reinforced when I caught sight of an extra-ordinary array of apparatus in the opposite corner of the hut. It was reminiscent of those early Frankenstein films. At one end of the bench which ran the length of the hut, standing about eighteen inches high, was a strange-looking transmitting valve, more of copper and brass than glass, within a web of stout rubber tubing and heavily insulated electrical cable. It was the klystron.

This type of powerful microwave thermionic valve was the invention of the Varian brothers in the USA, a derivative of the pioneering work on the cyclatron by Professor Ernest Lawrence and his team at Berkeley, California, the previous year.

Oliphant saw the possibilities of the klystron for producing a source of 10 centimetres and was able to bring back the necessary data from which one could be constructed in his Birmingham laboratory. It seemed that this would meet the requirements of the AMRE group and so Dee, not one to hang around, obtained a set of klystron drawings from Oliphant with whom he was well acquainted, and had a model built in double quick time at the Mond Laboratory at Cambridge. This whole process, from its origination in the States to Dee's model, was a fine example of the old pals' act brought to the aid of a good cause.

But what a monster! In the first place it was demountable and continuously evacuated which meant that a whole conglome-ration of vacuum oil diffusion and motor-driven backing pumps was needed. It was also water cooled because it was, we hoped, capable of high-power operation; a water pump was therefore necessary to circulate cooling water from a large cold-water cistern which stood outside the window. Hence the network of rubber tubing.

The most motley collection of equipment, however, stood down on the floor in the corner of the lab. This was the power supply for the klystron, which at this stage was operating as a continuous wave and not a pulsed device. As well as requiring a high accelerating voltage of the order of 20,000, being in the CW (continuous wave) mode, it also drew a considerable steady current. The power required was not far removed from that of a small broadcasting station, but because it had been hastily assembled from what could be begged or borrowed from a variety of places it had more the appearance of a jumble sale. There were oil-filled mains transformers the size of a tea chest, high-voltage capacitors the size and shape of a suitcase sprouting tall white porcelain insulators which in themselves were a sufficient warning of lethally high voltages. The whole Heath Robinson assembly was crowned with a gigantic rectifier valve not unlike those I had seen at the Rugby radio station.

Casting my eyes over this amazing array of apparatus on that first day in the hut on C site, I couldn't help remarking to Ward that I thought we were supposed to be working on something to go into an aeroplane. He made no comment – just smiled. It all made a disturbingly busy sound with its humming motors and clack-clack-clacking vacuum-backing pump, but all this mechanical activity was in vain, for the precious klystron stood proud and mute. It seemed that although the theory was simple enough, for the klystron to build up its powerful oscillation every facet of its construction, assembly and adjustment had to be just right. Here was the bane of many a scientist – an entity possessing an infinite number of variables.

Dee and Skinner, the joint group leaders, took their share with Bill Burcham and Jimmy Atkinson in trying to prod the klystron into action. Their individual approaches to the project mirrored their distinctive personalities. Skinner the eternal optimist would try anything, working persistently until achieving a result. Dee on the other hand was always critical and impatient for results but would not make a move until he had carefully and logically considered and discussed every possible alternative. Cockcroft, recognizing the value of their achievements, wrote of 'the Dee and Skinner team always furiously engaged in argument'; but he did so in the knowledge that it was always in a good-hearted manner. To the rest of us their lively discussions were most entertaining. They were always agreed, however, on the ultimate goal and the fact that no time must be lost to achieve it.

While the klystron party was engaged in its seemingly fruitless quest for transmitter power, Lovell and Chapman were busily occupied with the no less difficult task of producing a suitable aerial. Basically no new departure in established aerial practice was required for the aerial radiator itself, which would consist of a dipole and reflector – a miniature version of the familiar 'H' aerial of early TV days. What was vital however, was the manner in which the feeder cable was connected to the aerial elements; the length and disposition of the connections, marginal at longer wavelengths, became of major significance at 10 centimetres. Then there was the question of the best form of reflector – necessary to produce a narrow beam; should it be a horn or parabolic reflector? Both were tried before the parabolic mirror (often referred to as a dish) was adopted, the aerial itself supported on a stem twelve to eighteen inches long through which the feeder cable passed and which embodied a matching stub.

Lovell and Chapman were undoubtedly an ideal team for this task. Lovell himself possessed the dogged persistence in experimentation of Skinner, the organizational ability of Dee and the industriousness of Atkinson and Burcham. His greatest attribute, however, was his extreme enthusiasm for whatever project he was engaged in at any time. With these qualities one can appreciate how, when the war ended, he succeeded against great odds and governmental indifference in building the world's first giant radio telescope.

In Chapman, Lovell had a most valuable asset. A university laboratory assistant was truly a jack of all trades and master of them all. He combined the abilities of an instrument-maker, a tool-maker, a glass-blower, and an expert in vacuum technique. In addition he would have a working knowledge of electronics, optics and thermo-dynamics. To a university laboratory a good assistant would be as valuable as a master chef to a *maître d'hôtel.*

Chapman was all these things but above all he was by temperament calm and unflappable and in no way intimidated by Lovell's hyperactive zeal. Hence they made an effective and extremely productive team.

While arguments ranged on the feasibility or otherwise of klystrons, Lovell and Chapman were busy outside in the field most of the time testing one aerial model after another. Now and again Lovell would march into the hut triumphantly waving the latest of his centimetre aerials above his head and would declare loudly that it was a certain degree better than the previous day's model.

Meanwhile Dee was continuing to complain about the klystron and the futility of working on a device that could only be persuaded to oscillate 'for ten minutes once a fortnight.' This was no exaggeration, for in the three odd weeks that I'd seen the klystron in position at the end of the bench, I had witnessed it operating on only two occasions, and for no more than ten to twenty minutes on each occasion.

On the first of these occasions we heard Skinner shout: 'It's working!' We all gathered round and watched him take a screwdriver and draw off a spark from the tip of the output stub. Then we saw an amazing phenomenon that I had never witnessed previously. The power output at this very high radio frequency was such that the act of drawing off the spark ionized the air in the vicinity of the stub and the resulting corona gave the appearance of a blue spirit flame which remained visible for as long as the klystron continued to oscillate. Holding one's hand a few inches away one could feel heat; not the internal heat dissipated by the body of the klystron but the radio-frequency heating effect as in a present-day microwave oven.

The next question was how to transfer this power to an aerial. Coaxial cables of the type and quality then in existence were considered too lossy. The possibility of using a waveguide was considered. This was a whole new untried technique. The waveguide consisted of a hollow metal tube having a critical diameter along which the short radio waves could be propagated. It was decided to try one.

We needed several yards of metal tubing of about two inches diameter which for the purpose of the experiment was sufficiently close in terms of wavelength to what was required. At the time we were given to understand that we had acquired house gutter piping (in those days zinc) bought from Edgar's ironmongers' shop in Swanage. But many years later I was to learn from Jimmy Atkinson that it was vent piping belonging to Elsan chemical toilet kits. These were stocked in main stores, Elsans being the necessary form of sanitation at the Worth Matravers site. It was a typical example of the Atkinson flair for procurement, but since a number of kits had to be drawn in order to provide sufficient piping, he was left with a somewhat bizarre problem. The fact that we knew nothing of this at the time was doubtless in order not to offend the sensibilities of those involved with the experiment!

About twelve feet of the pipe was set up along the bench supported by laboratory retort stands, with the output stub of the klystron set across the mouth of the pipe. Skinner manipulated the various voltage and mechanical tuning adjustments until eventually the klystron burst into oscillation. Once again (and possibly for the last time) we were to witness the extraordinary power-generating capabilities of the Oliphant klystron. To check that power was being transmitted down the length of the makeshift waveguide a neon lamp was held across the far end of the pipe. The lamp glowed brightly from the effect of the high-frequency radiation (this being a recognized check for transmitter power output at any wavelength), but there was really little need for this since by holding one's hand within a couple of feet of the end of the pipe one could feel the heat – almost as if it were a blast of warm air.

With all this activity going on, Ward and I were encouraged to redouble our efforts. Having already tested a variety of valves operating in the Barkhausen–Kurz mode without success we had great hopes of a rather special consignment which had just been delivered. Included were some valves specifically designed for B–K operation, and furthermore at a wavelength of 18 centimetres, which was at least within the sphere of our interest.

The consignment was in fact a complete ultra-short-wave station which had been erected near Lympe in Kent shortly before the war as part of an Anglo-French cross-Channel telephone link. The valves in which we were interested were called Clavier tubes after their French inventor. They had been used both for the transmitter and for the receiver local oscillator.

At the outbreak of war the station had been dismantled and stored for the duration in the old R101 airship hangar at Cardington. With Tizard's backing Skinner eventually persuaded the Air Ministry to let us try the valves but they insisted that the whole station be kept intact.

Hence it was that several lorry loads of equipment arrived on our doorstep at C site. There were about half-a-dozen equipment racks full of electronics and controls, and in addition there were motor-generator sets, battery charging panels, a gigantic parabolic aerial system (fortunately in sections) and many odd pieces of pipe, cable and spare parts.

Skinner duly signed the paperwork and we set to work to see what could be done with these supposedly remarkable valves. Several years later someone else applied to borrow the same equipment. Doubtless he also had some influence, for the Air Ministry authorized its transfer. By this time it had been completely cannibalized. With components in short supply there was little point in giving houseroom to a static monster when it was bristling with meters, high-current variable resistors, and many more very useful parts. Even the parabolic aerial sections provided a useful source of aluminium. Whether one regarded this as wartime economy or pure vandalism is neither here nor there, but had it been peacetime the unfortunate Dr Skinner, who for the benefit of all had appended his name to the precious paperwork, could have found himself without a pension. In wartime, however, there was a simple mechanism for overcoming such administrative inconveniences; it was called 'enemy action'!

What of the precious valves? The odd ten or dozen of them which came were certainly useful even if they did not advance our researches a great deal, but their number gradually declined as they became victim to an assortment of fates.

All in all this unique equipment could be said to have been sacrificed in a worthy cause, both national and scientific, since our wartime researches would ultimately lead to a much improved technology for the proliferation of post-war telecommunication links.

Of all the oscillator valves tried in this series of experiments the only one to show any promise at all was a Western Electric type 3B/250-A, commonly known as a 'Samuel Tube'. It operated not by the Barkhausen–Kurz principle but in conventional fashion with a positive anode voltage of 250. It was called a 'double doorknob' by the Americans because of the shape of its glass envelope and because its electrode connections were brought out on both sides of the 'knob' by tungsten pins sealed into the glass. This configuration allowed it to be fitted midway between a pair of transmission lines which formed the tuned circuit.

There was, however, one snag. It was designed for wavelengths down to 1 metre. We managed to have it oscillating at a wavelength of 20 centimetres at which we could use the second harmonic in a 10 centimetre receiver, but this was at the cost of a serious reduction in efficiency. This meant that for a useful output level the valve ran excessively hot. In consequence it would run merrily for about half an hour before suddenly stopping due to the connections becoming oxidized – a shortcoming which could be a constant source of embarrassment.

As for finding a suitable type of signal detector, we did have a brief acquaintance with a thermionic device called a BO diode. The only one in existence and hence valued at £1,000 (over

£50,000 in today's money) had been lent to Ward by Standard Telephones and Cables. It had an exceptionally small clearance between filament and anode. Before we could get down to serious experiments with it I had committed the unthinkable – I blew it up! To my surprise and relief Ward just shrugged it off, saying he never thought it would work anyway. As for the price on its head, I presume it was marked down to our old friend enemy action! And so crystal detectors it was to be, a task taken on by Skinner himself who not only had the vision of what was required but the practical abilities, including glass-blowing skill, to make it.

The device had to be small and of a suitable linear shape to be fitted into some form of transmission line. The configuration which Skinner devised is in common use today in many semiconductor diodes (though not with the cat's whisker). After a degree of trial and error the method that Skinner adopted was remarkably simple. A small chipping of silicon crystal was bonded to a length of wire, and the cat's whisker was two or three open turns of thin tungsten wire forming a spring. The two parts were then sealed into a short length of glass tube with the tungsten spring tip in contact with the crystal, using glass-to-metal sealing technology. Half-way along the length of the tube a pimple of glass would be drawn off under the heat of a glassblower's flame and the tip broken off to leave a small hole.

Skinner would then test the device using the ubiquitous AVO test meter. He would measure the detector's resistance, first with the test leads connected in one direction and then taking a second reading with them reversed. Unlike a pure resistance which gives the same reading either way round, a crystal detector should read low in one direction and high in reverse. This is known as the 'front-to-back ratio' and this simple test has become standard procedure in the world of semiconductors. The greater the difference between the two readings, the better the detector.

Positioning the cat's whisker against the crystal while sealing both parts into the glass tube was a tricky business. Complete success with each device constructed was never assured. Some would show only a marginal difference between the two readings while others would have very high readings in both directions or conversely both might be very low. When a favourable set of readings was obtained on a particular model Skinner would gently tap the device several times to check that it was stable before filling the tube with molten wax through the pimple hole.

Many a long day Skinner would sit at a workbench making up his crystal assemblies with the aid of a glassblower's burner. As the hut did not enjoy all the facilities of a university lab, Skinner was obliged to supply the burner with a mixture of Calor gas and oxygen from a cylinder. Frequently we would be alarmed by a loud bang – it would be Skinner, getting rather too liberal with his oxygen. After a few days the bench would be littered with a large quantity of spent matches. How many were from relighting the burner and how many from relighting his pipe was anyone's guess!

The crystal detector as devised by Skinner was in due course developed for production by BTH. Ceramic tube replaced the glass, and metal end-caps facilitated mechanical assembly. No other device was to supplant the crystal detector throughout the war, and at the end of hostilities, attempts to determine how (and why) the humble crystal and cat's whisker actually worked led Schockley and his associates at Bell Laboratories to invent the transister in 1947. From its crude beginning the Skinner crystal was to become the seed corn of the age of the semiconductor.

It now remained to devise a suitable form of mixer unit embodying a Skinner crystal. With such a unit the incoming signal would be combined with the output from Ward's local oscillator to produce a lower frequency output capable of being amplified. Such a method had been standard practice in radio sets since the early thirties, but nothing like a centimetre mixer had yet been produced.

With a combination of complex mathematics and plumbing in roughly equal proportions Burcham and his team got busy fashioning a series of trial configurations from small pieces of brass tubing carefully soldered together. Minute errors in dimensions or proportions would at such high frequencies result in a serious loss of efficiency which, because the received signals were weak, would prove disastrous. Eventually a workable design was established, giving physical substance to the mathematical concept.

At last the receiver was taking shape, albeit crudely, but what of the transmitter?

6 The Breakthrough

It was a bright sunny morning on 19 July when Jimmy Atkinson was seen to clear some bench space near the monumental klystron to make way for a new and exciting toy – one which was to have a profound effect on the scientific war – the cavity magnetron.

In searching for a solution to the complexities and limitations of the klystron, two members of Professor Oliphant's team at Birmingham University, J.T. Randall and H.A.H. Boot, had been considering the possibility of applying the principle of resonant cavities to another and earlier type of high-frequency oscillator valve called a magnetron. Some work had been carried out before the war on a device called a split-anode magnetron by a number of workers including Yagi in Japan and Megaw in England. With this type a tuned circuit was connected across the two halves of the valve anode which was placed within a strong magnetic field. The effect of this was to make the electrons emitted from the cathode take up an orbital path and hence circulate between the two semicircular halves of the split anode. The tuned circuit connected across the two halves would hence become excited.

With this basically simple device there was a practical limit to how small a tuned circuit could be fitted externally across the valve envelope and hence how short a wavelength the magnetron could generate. It occurred to Randall and Boot however, that if the anode took the form of a resonant cavity, this would be equivalent to building the tuned circuit into the anode itself.

This is exactly what Randall and Boot did, and with the aid of improvised equipment to provide a high voltage and a powerful magnetic field, at their very first attempt on 21 February 1940 it worked. Sufficient power to light a car headlamp bulb was produced and when the wavelength was measured (using lecher lines) it was 9.8 centimetres.

So little more than four months later, this was why Jimmy Atkinson was clearing the bench. After the obstinate klystron the magnetron was so delightfully simple to operate that calling it a toy was not inappropriate.

The model which Jimmy had for our first trials was a production prototype which had been made by GEC under the supervision of Megaw who was to visit us a few days later to check on its performance. Fashioned out of solid copper it was the size and shape of a pill box with cooling fins around its circumference. The filament connections were brought out from one side through glass seals, and an output stub from the opposite side also through a glass seal. The magnetic field was provided by a specially made permanent magnet in the shape of a flattened horseshoe eight by five inches in size.

A simple cradle made of wood was to support the magnetron between the poles of the magnet. Cooling air was provided by an industrial hot-air blower (with the heating element removed). This was an RAF stores stock item from the days when aircraft were of wood and doped canvas, which called for accelerated drying of repairs. As for the high-voltage supply, conveniently that provided for the klystron filled the bill.

With the precious magnetron in position and connected up, Jimmy began to wind up the high-voltage supply. One thousand, two thousand ... nine thousand, ten ... Suddenly a neon lamp being held against the output stub of the magnetron started to glow: the magnetron was oscillating, producing power − 10 centimetre power! It was all so simple, unbelievably simple. We didn't audibly cheer but nevertheless that was the feeling we all shared. We all knew that from that moment centimetre RDF was about to take off.

We now had all the essential ingredients of a system: the magnetron transmitter soon to be provided with a more compact power supply with a modulator whose function was to apply the high voltage in regular short pulses; a receiver, albeit one having a local oscillator that was not as dependable as we would have wished; and Lovell's aerials which had now reached near perfection.

There were a number of four-wheel mobile RDF trailers in surplus and two of these were obtained and positioned in line outside the hut broadside on to the headland. The sides opened out in the manner of a mobile coffee stall which made them ideal for field work. They were called 'GL trailers' although systems other than gun-laying radars were accommodated in their type.

The magnetron transmitter was installed in one of the trailers and our receiver in the other. Mains supplies to each were fed out from the hut. Initially the transmitter and receiver each had a separate aerial system consisting of one of Lovell's dipoles mounted in a three-foot diameter aluminium parabolic reflector. Later a twin assembly on a steerable mounting complete with a crosswire site would become available, but in the meantime the separate aerials had to be individually trained on to a target by their respective operators. This situation was to hamper operation in the first instance and to make it difficult to track moving objects; nevertheless, results were immediate and exciting.

At first the aerials were trained on the ancient Norman chapel and the adjacent eighteenth century terrace of coastguard cottages on St Alban's headland about a mile distant. Adjustments were made, the receiver tuned, and then there was great excitement as the first crop of echoes appeared on the cathode-ray oscilloscope. Here at last was centimetre RDF, simple and crude maybe, but something on which to build.

It was straightforward enough for the two aerial operators standing down on the ground outside their respective trailers to line up their aerials on the group of buildings not far distant which produced well-defined blips, responding to prompting from whoever was observing the oscilloscope inside the receiver trailer to obtain a maximum signal. It was quite a different ball game when attempting to follow a moving target with such a ponderous process. Echoes from the occasional ship sailing past the headland were obtained, and if the aerials were suitably trained down the field, responses could be received from vehicles passing up or down the track leading to the headland.

Yet attempts to track an Anson aircraft on test flights from the Telecommunications Flying Unit at nearby Christchurch proved abortive even though the Anson was a relatively slow machine and by instruction was flying at heights of only 1,000 and 2,000 feet. Simultaneous targeting by the separate operators was found impossible in these cases.

It was imperative that convincing demonstrations of the new technology should be given to the various influential parties as soon as possible, for there were disbelievers in high places. There were those who considered that prime scientific effort should not be wasted on way-out projects such as centimetre RDF. Waiting for the odd ship that might just happen to pass by would be no way to impress impatient VIPs.

We had persisted with this abortive test procedure for several frustrating days when the time came for Dee, Skinner, Atkinson and Ward to travel to London for a meeting at the GEC Research Laboratories at Wembley. GEC had been awarded a development contract by the Air Ministry for a centimetre airborne system. Unfortunately for Dee, Skinner and Co., GEC Wembley had already been working on a 25 centimetre system previously initiated by Bowen and they had no desire (nor indeed intention) to drop a promising venture in favour of some hair-brained 10 centimetre set-up concocted by a 'bunch of academic nuts' who knew nothing about radio. Yet the mathematics left no doubt in the minds of our people that nothing greater than 10 centimetres in wavelength would do the job – to say nothing of Skinner's vision of 1 centimetre.

While the others were away at Wembley, Lovell and Burcham were making further attempts at tracking an aircraft. I had been helping, it was early afternoon and a spirit of depression was abroad since once again our efforts had come to nought. What was needed was a moving target, not too fast, and one which could be called up to order. This gave me an idea – I suggested to Lovell that I might fix a small sheet of aluminium to the side of my bicycle and so equipped, cycle around the headland as a moving target. Lovell was non-committal and shrugged his shoulders. I had the impression that he saw no validity to such a scheme.

In the spirit of 'try anything once' I wired the piece of metal to my machine and set off down the roadway towards the headland. The rough track ran down the left-hand side of the field and at the far end it dropped down into a hollow which gave access to a quarry lower down to the right. The roadway to the headland was straight ahead however, and a short sharp climb brought one back on to the wide plateau which was the headland area. Since the 1960s this area on both sides of the roadway has been enclosed and cultivated but previously it was wild scrubland covered with clumps of gorse, heather and thorn among sparse dry grass. None of the clumps were more than knee high on account of the constant salt-laden breezes which effectively stunted their growth. Across this wild moorland I had no difficulty in cycling, although needing to zig-zag between the clumps.

I was now cycling broadside-on to the trailers with their aerial dishes, which I could see about three-quarters of a mile away. I made several stops in order to give Lovell and Burcham time to train their aerials in my direction. I even dismounted and lifted the cycle with its reflector to shoulder height to offer the maximum degree of reflection.

These antics must have lasted at least a half-hour before I made the journey back. Arriving back at the trailers I was disappointed and annoyed to find them shut up and deserted. Lovell was standing outside the hut just looking out into space. 'Weren't you watching me?' I asked testily. 'Of course,' he replied unconvincingly, 'echoes up to saturation' ('saturation' meaning the strongest possible signal). This to me was so unlikely as to be unbelievable and I took it that Lovell was just being patronizing. I felt foolish.

The next morning four very dejected physicists arrived back

from their Wembley meeting. It transpired that GEC had won a moral victory. Whilst Dee and Skinner had little by way of positive results to report, GEC had taken them up on to the roof of the Wembley building where their 25 centimetre system was set up in a hut. Here they were shown an impressive array of echoes from the surrounding topography.

Under these circumstances it was difficult to make a convincing argument as to why the firm should drop their promising 25 centimetre system in order to take up the TRE 10 centimetre, which at that time looked remarkably like a non-starter.

At that moment Lovell interrupted them. 'You should have had GEC down here yesterday,' he proclaimed and went on to describe my performance of the previous afternoon and its results. So he hadn't kidded me after all. I was as delighted with this news as the others. Straightaway I had to strap the sheet of aluminium to my bicycle once again and make a repeat performance for the benefit of the four incredulous scientists to whom life after death had just been granted.

'We must certainly get GEC down here,' insisted Dee, and get them down they did. Once again I had to put on my circus act. Grudgingly the firm agreed there might be some future in the 10 centimetre system but they were not going to capitulate without displaying their presumed technical superiority. This consisted of advice as to where improvements could be made and where certain losses of power might be avoided. In so doing they expressed the degree of improvement or loss in terms of decibels – dBs for short.

This was a red rag to the academic bull. It wasn't that our university researchers were unaware of what a decibel was, but in their work they embraced a much wider field of observation and measurement in which multiplication factors were more appropriate. For radio and communication engineers however, the decibel system was ideal, since being a logarithmic system a succession of gains or losses throughout a circuit or along a transmission line which had been measured in dBs could be summed by simple addition or subtraction.

Here therefore was a source of professional snobbery between the two camps – the tough commercial world of the professional engineer and the relaxed *laissez-faire* atmosphere of the university campus. Hence it was that next day Skinner announced to all of us in the lab: 'dBs will not be used as a unit of measurement in this laboratory.' Tribal loyalties therefore ensured that the humble decibel was banished from our midst for the duration of the war – it was with GEC, not Hitler!

From the time of this first demonstration to GEC a veritable avalanche of interested parties descended upon us. This presented us with a catch-22 situation by which a continuous succession of visitors was holding up the work; yet without these visitors, all of whom were influential, the necessary backing for continued development of centimetre RDF might not be forthcoming.

Predictably one of the first VIPs to come was Watson-Watt who in his capacity as Director of Communications Development (DCD) at the Ministry was responsible for the work at TRE and other establishments. He was a stockily built Scot with dark curly hair and was smartly dressed in a navy-blue suit as befitted the scientist turned administrator. He arrived accompanied by an intimidating array of army and air force senior officers, personal assistants in smart suits, and of course A.P. Rowe and Dr Lewis with their respective PAs. The whole impressive entourage had the air of a royal visit, but then in the world of RDF Watson-Watt *was* royalty.

Like a circus performer, given my cue, I was off bumping over the rough ground on my faithful machine. By now we had between us developed a recognized routine to ensure a successful demonstration. At the point on the route where the track dipped down into the hollow by the quarry I was out of sight for several minutes. While out of sight, my radar echo seen on the cathode-ray tube lost little of its magnitude, and this provided a striking feature to each demonstration. The army representatives were particularly impressed and began excited discussions on the possibilities of detecting enemy tanks approaching from behind hills.

After struggling manfully with the two separate aerials, the day eventually came when the planned twin-mirror mounting arrived from workshops complete with two new shiny, bright aluminium parabolic mirrors, which after long delays had finally made their way from the manufacturers. They had been on a veritable mystery tour of England via a whole series of railway lines and possibly the odd canal barge too (for even the ancient canal system had been pressed into service to relieve the log jam in the transportation of war material). At one stage a day spent by Lovell on the telephone had failed to locate their presence, but there was great relief when eventually they turned up at Swanage station.

Here was another turning point. Although by this time it had been discovered that the aluminium sheet fixed to the bicycle did not significantly add to the amount of energy reflected back from my body, I was soon to become redundant as a circus performer. Now that we had the smart new twin-mirror aerial system with a business-like 'gun-site,' we were at long last able to track aircraft with a single operator.

We now had a memorable visit from Professor Lindemann in his capacity as scientific advisor to the Prime Minister, an appointment made by Winston Churchill upon becoming premier. Lindemann had long been a friend of the Churchill family. On a professional footing Churchill had constantly valued Lindemann's advice on technical and scientific matters, particularly during what Churchill himself described as his 'wilderness years' when as a back-bencher in the 1930s he was concerned about Britain's lack of preparedness.

The professor, undoubted genius that he was, was nevertheless on first appearance the perfect manifestation of the fictional 'mad scientist.' Arriving in the heart of rural England, he appeared incongruously dressed in black coat and striped trousers, complete with rolled-up umbrella – for all the world like a city gent, but with his bowler hat worn carelessly on the back of his head.

He was tall, lean, greying and with a clipped grey moustache, but wiry and energetic. I had the impression that he was one of the disbelievers, but this *bête noir* of the Tizard Committee had no obstinacy of mind; his incisive intellect was about to size up the capabilities of the new technique. Doubtless his on-the-spot judgement would determine whether or not centimetres were for this war, for his report would most likely end up on the desk of the prime minister.

Any fears that he might be biased against the system, for this was the work of Cavendish men, were soon to be dispelled; the rival Clarendon professor from Oxford was highly enthusiastic about what he witnessed.

No longer performing on my bicycle, my job was to keep the receiver in tune and to do this I was to have a privileged position. In the darkened receiver trailer I sat within view of the cathode-ray tube display with one hand on the tuning knob (and with the book of common prayer in my pocket!) with the hope and purpose of keeping our dreaded oscillator running. Should it pack up the whole demonstration would be aborted.

The professor was not content merely to stand and view the tube from a discreet distance but sat himself on the upturned wooden crate immediately beside me. Pushing his bowler even farther back on his head, he leaned forward to take a critical look at the display.

The display was what was called an 'A scope'. This is the basic form of radar display in which the spot on the screen travels rapidly and repeatedly from left to right in synchronism with the transmitted pulses. At a typical repetition rate of 1,000 times per second this 'time base' appears as a continuous line. Any output from the receiver would deflect the spot vertically, forming a shape like a stalagmite (stalagmites go upwards), popularly known as a 'blip'. As well as received pulses (i.e. echoes) from discreet objects such as buildings, those from aircraft and ships would have a height dependent partly on their size and reflectivity, but principally on their distance. To obtain a maximum range of detection the receiver would have a high order of sensitivity with the result that the time base would not appear as a nice, sharp, thin line but due to receiver background noise and the sum total of echoes from minor features such as bushes, trees, rocks, and, when over the sea, the tops of waves, the line would be broken up into what was known as 'clutter'. As the colour of the trace on most cathode-ray tubes was green, the appearance of this jagged line was not unlike grass, a term which was sometimes used to describe it. When searching for distant targets one was looking initially for a very small but recurring blip amongst the clutter. This was almost like searching for the proverbial needle in the haystack.

It therefore amazed and surprised us that Lindemann was the first to spot the incoming target aircraft flying in over the sea from several miles out. 'There it is,' he shouted with excitement, nearly jumping off his seat and pointing to the small blip almost submerged in the clutter. We watched it grow bigger and steadier, gradually moving from right to left until at minimum range the now very strong echo was swallowed up by the large transmitter pulse, which stood permanently at the left-hand end of the tube trace. Almost immediately we heard the roar of the plane's twin engines as the Anson from Christchurch passed low overhead.

The plane flew a variety of courses at a modest altitude in the course of the demonstration, which proceeded without a hitch. We also showed the professor the regular features including echoes from the coastguard houses and St Aldhelm's chapel, but nothing further matched the excitement and triumph of that first sighting.

From this moment onwards were were never to look back; neither would it be the last visit from this Oxford professor, but the next time he would come as Lord Cherwell, an honour bestowed upon him the following year.

Another visit which comes to mind was that from Professor Oliphant. This was in the nature of a family visit and an occasion when everyone was relaxed. It was a particularly hot day and the burly grey-haired Australian arrived literally in a cloud of dust. Having been 'shown the works', the circle of friends, – Oliphant, Dee and Skinner – repaired to the cool shade of the hut to inspect the various bits and pieces being worked upon and to continue the discussion on further developments of centimetre techniques. The professor's eyes lit up as Skinner asked 'Would you like some tea Oliphant?' but he was somewhat deflated when, a few minutes later, Skinner handed him what looked like a cup full of creosote, with the words 'Sorry, we've no milk or sugar'.

In retrospect this period of pioneering demonstrations was a most momentous time. Little did any of us realize at the time that history was being made. The dawn of centimetre radar was to be a whole new epoch. It was in no way a progression from existing radio techniques but a new science. However, as impressive and successful as our demonstrations had been, in one respect we had been sailing very close to the wind, on account of our temperamental receiver oscillator. Ward and I put on years from anxiety each time there was an important demonstration.

There was one occasion when we nearly didn't get away with it. It was possibly the Watson-Watt visit. For about two days the oscillator had been playing up more than usual. So concerned about it was Ward that quite late the evening before, he and Jimmy Atkinson called on me at my lodgings for a council of war. It was decided that Ward and I should get into work extra early the next morning to give the offending machine a thorough overhaul.

Well before the appointed time of the visitors' arrival we had it running and so we all felt quite pleased with ourselves. Then just as the visiting party were approaching in the customary cloud of dust the wretched thing stopped oscillating. 'Heck!' cried Ward, 'the only thing to help us now is for the siren to go off.'

No sooner had he uttered the cry of agony as the convoy of cars was turning into our field than, as if by act of the deity, the deep wail of the siren sounded.

There was a brief conference between the visitors, Rowe's staff, and our own people. The VIPs, having made a long tiring journey, made it known that they had no intention of being put off by Hitler. Meanwhile Ward and I had switched off the supplies, counted ten (taking about two minutes to do so) and switched on again. To our great relief it burst into oscillation and thankfully kept going long enough to carry through the demonstration. And that was the closest we ever got to disaster.

Help however was to hand, seemingly out of the blue as if our repeated prayers had at long last been answered.

The day had started much as most others. Ward had come to me with a hastily scribbled circuit, asking me to wire it up as soon as possible for it to be ready for some visitors who would arrive later that morning. The circuit was very similar to that used to supply a small cathode-ray tube, having an overall voltage of a thousand or thereabouts and a couple of intermediate voltage controls.

About eleven o'clock two gentlemen arrived, one carrying a briefcase. They had come from the Admiralty Signals Establishment at Bristol and their names were Sutton and Thompson. They were not solicitors as the combination of their names might suggest, though they could easily be taken as such, but they were specialists in thermionic valve research. The formalities of welcome having been quickly disposed of, the briefcase was duly opened and a somewhat strange-looking valve produced.

It had a glass envelope an inch in diameter and about six inches long with a standard five-pin valveholder at one end. But sealed into the glass half-way along its length was an assembly of copper and brass the shape of a ring doughnut. We gingerly clamped it to a retort stand and I made the connections to the supplies which had been prepared.

So far there was nothing apparently high-frequency in the set-up, just a matter of supplying DC voltages via any odd lengths of wire. Thompson checked the connections, nodding approval and we switched on. Into a hole at the edge of the brass ring which clamped the outer edges of the copper doughnut he inserted a small loop of wire soldered to a flash-lamp bulb (what the Americans called a 'pea lamp') and began to adjust the voltage controls. Very soon the lamp started to glow. 'There we are,' declared Sutton, '10 centimetres or thereabouts.'

After our weeks of trauma in trying to keep our 20 centimetre oscillator going this was sheer magic. Just like the magnetron, here was something outwardly simple and which could be made to work to order. Here at last was the missing link.

Thompson called it a Sutton tube (for Sutton was his senior) whilst Sutton said he called it the Thompson tube since Thompson had done most of the work on it. Later it was to be given the official title of 'reflecting klystron' for it was just that.

The copper doughnut was a resonant cavity; a brass screw on one side of the brass clamping ring served as a fine-tuning control according to the amount of its length entering the cavity. The concept of the single resonator with a reflecting electrode at the further end of the tube was as clever as it was simple. Whereas its big brother the klystron depended on the correct interaction of its twin resonators, the Sutton tube relied principally on the electron optics within the tube for successful operation, the parameters of which could easily be set externally by the voltage controls.

It took only part of the morning for the staging of this remarkable test for Ward to become fully acquainted with the operating parameters of this novel device. So after being shown around the lab, our two benefactors departed for lunch and the journey back to Bristol.

With Randall and Boot's magnetron, Skinner's crystal, and now Sutton and Thompson's reflecting klystron, we had the ingredients of a practical and reliable system. All that remained (to underestimate the task) was to engineer everything into a suitable form for installation in an aircraft. This would include devising some form of high-frequency switch which would allow the use of a single common aerial for both transmission and reception. This would take time and effort in the weeks ahead, but what was important was that 10 centimetre transmission and reception was now an accomplished fact.

7   Al Fresco

The Dorset coast in the glorious summer of 1940 was idyllic: warm sunny days and clear blue skies, nature's compensation for the previous hard winter. We all took advantage of this beautiful weather and as well as taking our sandwich lunches out of doors, many of us fresh from smoky cities (there was no Clean Air Act before the war) succumbed to the novelty of working al fresco as work permitted. The season Bawdsey brigade were already adapted to this delightful way of life and it was not unusual to see the superintendent holding a high-level meeting out on the grass. Seated in a wide circle, they would remind me of my Wolf Cub days, except that they were seated on office chairs and not with crossed legs on the ground.

On C site our field was a veritable hub of outdoor activity. Aerial measurements had to be done out in the field and so Lovell and Chapman were glad of the ideal weather for this activity. The rest of us, if we had jobs which could be taken outside, did so. Meetings and discussions were much improved by generous amounts of fresh Dorset air.

Soon the shooting war was to arrive on our doorstep. At first there were sporadic raids by small numbers of enemy aircraft, on selected targets such as the naval dockyard at Portland, and attacks on shipping coming up the Channel. By August came the big raids; the Battle of Britain had begun. The siren would sound and before many minutes had elapsed we would hear the deep humming of the armada. Always to the south-east, we would look towards the direction of the sound, scanning the blue sky. There they would be, a hardly discernible mass of dots high in the heavens. Gradually the sound would grow in intensity and soon the shapes of the individual planes could be seen. There would be formations of bombers, mainly Heinkels but frequently augmented with Junkers and the slimmer Dorniers. These formations would be surrounded by groups of defending Messerschmitt 109 fighters. We would start counting: 10, 20, 30, 40; it was difficult to count beyond 60 but frequently these raids would involve more than a hundred aircraft.

These great armadas always appeared to be heading in our direction as if homing in on our site, but before they had reached the coast our Spitfires and Hurricanes would sweep in with the familiar whine of their Rolls Royce engines to break up the Luftwaffe formations before engaging in individual combat.

High up on our prominent headland we had a grandstand view of these battles. Above the undulating whine of aero-engines we would hear the sharp staccato sound of the eight machine-gun multiples of the British fighters and the thump-thump of the ME 109s' cannon fire as the combatants weaved, dived, and climbed, seeking to manoeuvre their opponents within the field of their gunsights.

We would watch with fascination as this drama unfolded before our eyes, but with no more feeling than if it had been a football match. The summer sun, the green fields, the blue sea all added to the unreality of the scene. But high up in the sky men were locked in mortal battle; machines and men were being ripped apart, plunging to earth in balls of fire. Watching from our distance – two, maybe three miles away – we were detached as one would be watching a wild-west film. The spectacle was sanitized by distance – the blood was not seen, we were not the ones with the guns, shooting or being shot, killing or being killed.

But for these engagements over the sea, the great armadas would be unloading their deadly cargoes upon inland towns and cities. Thanks to the work of the Bawdsey pioneers only a minority of enemy bombers got through to cause havoc. Later, when the Luftwaffe would be driven to making their raids by night, the RAF's ability to intercept would be minimal compared to daylight engagements. Much suffering would be endured by the inhabitants of London and other major cities until an effective airborne radar became a reality. The work of our group was therefore to take on even greater urgency.

During these weeks of the Battle of Britain, A.P. Rowe was a very worried man. Guardian for the duration of a significant proportion of the country's top scientific and technical manpower, he was only too aware of the serious consequences should the Luftwaffe decide to deposit their lethal cargo on to his establishment. The fact that they always appeared to be heading straight for the site underlined his concern.

It seemed, however, that the TRE site was being used as a landmark, for on the occasions when the RAF had not engaged the bombers before they crossed the coastline they would vector off towards a selected target inland. It seemed to us incredible that the Luftwaffe could be ignorant of the purpose and importance of the establishment and were prepared to leave it unmolested. We now know however, how ineffective was German espionage.[1] They had (fortunately for us) a dearth of agents and sympathizers in this country and there was no co-ordinating organization within the Reich capable of feeding information gathered through to the right quarter.

There was nevertheless a danger from showers of stray bullets which, descending from a considerable height, could be as lethal as if actually aimed at the site. A member of the transmitter group had a lucky escape as one such bullet piercing the hut roof buried itself into the concrete floor not far from his feet.

At this time there were no air-raid shelters on site and our instructions were, at the sound of the warning, to evacuate buildings and disperse. Not that there was much in the way of natural shelter across this barren stretch of the Dorset coast. From our hut on C site we would repair to the dry-stone wall which formed the eastern boundary of the field. Here we would crouch under sheltering blackthorn bushes which would hardly protect one from the rain let alone bullets and bombs. However, we could still follow the action above while being entertained on the ground by the customary lively debates between Dee and Skinner as to the next step necessary to achieve our goal. Not even the Luftwaffe were allowed to interrupt their proceedings.

Doubtless in response to Rowe's great concern for his staff a crash programme of air-raid shelter building was initiated. These were underground shelters constructed of prefabricated concrete sections. Most of us were reluctant to descend into their dim interior, preferring not to miss any of the action, but a station order making the use of the shelters obligatory promptly put an end to our reckless behaviour.

Between 12 and 16 August the Luftwaffe staged a series of raids on the south-coast CH stations. Presumably they had now realized the effectiveness of the British RDF system, but the only surprise on our part was that they had not adopted this tactic much earlier. One morning during this period a station notice was passed round urgently from hand-to-hand. It was an account of such a raid on the nearby Ventor CH station, written by one of their senior officers. The gist of the message was that since the only casualties had been those caught unprotected out of doors by shrapnel and flying fragments, and that the first bombs fell almost immediately after the warning sounded, at the first sound of the siren staff should lose no time in getting to a shelter or blast-protected building. This warning was timely and relevant since the TRE site had the same type of aerial towers and buildings and indeed part of the main site had become operational since Dunkirk; it was therefore likely to be next on the Luftwaffe's list.

That same afternoon the siren sounded whereupon, cognizant of the Ventnor message, those of us working out in the field lost no time in hoofing it to the air-raid shelter. It was not our turn for an attack that afternoon; in fact we were left unmolested for about another eighteen months until one lunch time the site was subject to a 'hit and run raid' by a single Focke Wulf 190. The raid followed a familiar pattern. The aircraft swept in low from over the sea, releasing the bombs slung beneath its wings whilst strafing the area with cannon fire. The bombs fell just outside the perimeter fence, hitting the RAF cookhouse and causing some casualties. There was no warning – these lone raiders would fly in low below radar cover. The sound of the cannon fire at close quarters was quite alarming, causing everyone to dive for cover.

The Battle of Britain continued its violent course into September, during which time the Luftwaffe sustained untold losses. This was not, however, without the sacrifice of many of our fighter pilots – young men of my own age.

Hitler was anxious to launch his Operation Sealion and so the pressure was on Reich Marshal Goering to win the battle in the air. Having failed to defeat the RAF in daylight over the coast he changed his tactics, directing his attacks on inland industrial targets and resorting mainly to night raids.

On Saturday 7 September London experienced in violent fashion the start of the blitz, which was to last for many months to come. The first waves that afternoon brought havoc and destruction to both the docks and the City. That night the fires which lit the sky were to be seen across the length and breadth of the metropolis as the Luftwaffe continued the attack.

The government had previously been aware that this same weekend could possibly herald the start of Hitler's threatened invasion. Plans for the evacuation of TRE to an unspecified inland venue were hence put in train. To make the best use of available transport it was arranged for those with cars to take a full complement of passengers from among colleagues who were living in their locality.

Instructions were given for each of us to have a case packed ready with the minimum of clothes and personal effects to reduce bulk and weight. We were also advised to dispose of any personal documents which would connect us with our employment. Only our official passes were to be retained for the time being. Following these instructions I spent an evening in my room and having packed some essential items, made a fire of letters and other documents in the bedroom grate.

The establishment's secret files, which were normally kept in the registry during the silent hours, were packed into a trailer where they would be ready to take to the road at a moment's notice. Plans were made for key items of equipment to be similarly removed, or destroyed if removal was impractical. Doubtless our precious magnetron would have made its exodus in Dee's pocket since he lived nearest to the site in Worth village, but for the fact that he had just been struck down with pneumonia. Frantically Bill Burcham chased all around Swanage to find someone with an ambulance prepared to take off at a moment's notice to some completely unspecified place.

Having made all these necessary preparations for possible invasion we carried on with our work each day as normal, but the secret files continued to be kept and guarded in the trailers overnight with towing vehicles at the ready. How long it was before the order to stand down was given I cannot remember but we were to learn after the war that on 14 September Hitler personally postponed Sealion until the 17th, only then to postpone it further. The problems were proving insuperable and so by the 20th dispersion of the invasion fleet was begun.

Nothing was known of these things and ignorance inevitably fuelled a crop of wild rumours such as destroyer flotillas which had engaged large invasion fleets, or high-speed motor torpedo boats which had caused havoc among hordes of enemy barges. Needless to say, the reports were invariably claimed as authentic by someone who had known someone who was there.

The final turning point in the Battle of Britain was on 15 September when the Luftwaffe suffered the record number of 185 planes lost in a single day (although this number has since been in dispute). It was a significant victory for the RAF although not achieved without cost to itself, but never again was Germany to attempt mass daylight raids over this country.

By the end of October as the days shortened, nightly raids by the Luftwaffe on all our major cities became the norm and the word 'blitz' entered the English language. For Londoners it was a nightly occurrence, for other cities like Coventry wholesale destruction was suffered on a single night of terror.

It seemed that the Luftwaffe could bomb any of our cities at night with impunity. Anti-aircraft gunfire was quite ineffective in scoring hits, indeed the shrapnel from the exploding shells rained down and was just another hazard for the unfortunate citizens below. Its only value seemed to be as a morale booster on account of the sound of firing.

RAF night-fighters which were equipped with 1½ metre AI also proved to be of limited effect, due to the basic restrictions of the system as well as the performance of the older Blenheims. There was hence no question that 10 centimetre AI was needed, and needed fast.

Footnote

1. Jock Haswell, *The Intelligence and Deception of the D-Day Landings,* 1979.

8   The Stables

As the Battle of Britain reached a crescendo, A.P. Rowe's concern for the safety of his valuable staff, and for the precious hours being lost in air-raid shelters, also reached its peak. A policy of dispersal was the firm decision at an urgently convened meeting of his senior staff.

Accordingly the premises of a local private preparatory school were found to be ideal and were duly requisitioned – yet another task for the constantly overworked Mr A.B. Jones.

Leeson House, situated in its own well-wooded grounds on the road between Swanage and the village of Langton Matravers, was the school in question. Originally built in the seventeenth century, it was enlarged and flourished as the home of a rich family early in the nineteenth century. It had much to commend it, apart from the fact that by the time every group which did not specifically require any of the facilities of the Worth Matravers site (such as the aerial towers) had been moved down, space was at a premium.

Every corner, outhouse and gardener's hut was put to use; our group was lucky – we were allocated the stables!

The stables were an unmistakable sign of past eighteenth century affluence, perfect in the symmetry of their design. The building was a short distance from the house and surrounded by a high Purbeck stone wall which enclosed a courtyard. Projecting from each side of a two-storey centre section was a stable which accommodated four horses, and at each extremity was a coach-house with tall double doors. The gabled centre portion featured an archway which gave access to the two stables and at its far end the entrance to the groom's quarters which included a ground-floor living room and upstairs bedroom. Above the archway was a hay loft with an external hatchway for loading purposes.

Much conversion work was necessary before the place was fit for scientists to replace horses. Stalls were removed, floors levelled and concreted and openings made in the blank rear walls for windows. Long benches were fitted all around, power points and lighting fitted, and for heating, a large circular cast-iron coke-stove with smoke stack was installed in the middle of each room. This provided us with two large, spacious labs.

As for the two coach-houses, each had an interconnecting door knocked through to their adjoining stables, each a window put into the rear wall, a small coke-stove installed against the end wall, and light and power wired in. And as far as these two end rooms were concerned, that was all. Untouched were the flagstone floors which made it like working in a rock garden, and the tall coach-house doors stood as they had for about a hundred and fifty years: ill-fitting and draughty.

Another assistant, Alan Edmunds – a tall and lively fellow – had joined the group at Worth about a month after myself. He and I made ourselves at home in one of these end rooms. We found some sacking which helped to draught-proof the door, and to work on we had some barrack tables from main stores – those ubiquitous folding tables which would each seat six soldiers or airmen for meals. The other end room was equipped as a group workshop. Here the coach-house doors were ideal for bringing in machinery and materials.

The two rooms comprising the groom's quarters provided ideal if otherwise cramped office accommodation for Dee, Skinner, Lovell, and Atkinson. Each room had its original fireplace which in wintertime was put to good use.

Overall we had much more space than the single hut at Worth Matravers C site and in this respect we were more fortunate than those groups elsewhere in Leeson House and its outbuildings, where everyone was packed in like rush-hour commuters. With our increased accommodation, in the spirit of Parkinson's Law our numbers expanded to fill the space allotted to us.

The first of the new faces were those of Curran and Hensby who arrived from Exeter, where at an outstation of RAE they had been developing an electronic proximity fuse for bombs and AA shells. Dr Sam Curran was a sincere, well-mannered Scot; he was another star from the Cavendish firmament, having done research there from 1937 to 1939. Later in the war he would cross the Atlantic to take part in the Manhattan Project and would continue after the war to follow a very full career in nuclear physics, becoming the inventor of the scintillation counter, one of many achievements. To those unacquainted with nuclear matters this may be meaningless, but as a radiation detector it has greater significance than the more familiar Geiger counter. Since the war he has been honoured by becoming FRS; FRSE; Principal and Vice Chancellor of Strathclyde University; and in 1970 he was knighted.

His wife Joan, who was a talented scientist and mathematician in her own right, also came to work at TRE, where she made a significant contribution by her work on 'Window'. This was the codename for the bunches of aluminium foil strips which, when scattered from an aircraft, would fool the enemy's radar by producing echoes indistinguishable from those from aircraft. By the time of the Allied invasion of Normandy this had become a refined art by which massed raiders approaching the enemy coast in the Calais area were effectively simulated – an electronic decoy duck.

Curran's colleague Hensby was to become involved with flight trials once the centimetre equipment had reached the stage of development, where it could be flown in aircraft. Tragically this was to lead to his untimely death in the crash of an experimental aircraft in 1942.

A notable addition to the group's strength was the remarkable Alan Hodgkin. Remarkable because he was a biologist – a discipline as far from electronics as it was possible to imagine. Yet he showed himself to be an inspired and outstanding electronic-circuit designer. After the war he returned to work in his own discipline which led him to become a joint Nobel prizewinner for Medicine. He became a Fellow of the Royal Society, Master of Trinity, Chancellor of Leicester and was knighted. He was nevertheless a most charming and unassuming individual.

To assist Alan Hodgkin came another clever 'circuit man', a junior scientific officer (JSO) by the name of J.V. Jelley. Of slight build and elfin appearance, he too was very friendly and a most interesting conversationalist.

Skinner himself set about organizing the workshop. He managed to obtain an allocation of basic machine tools which included a good lathe, an electric grinder, and a drilling machine which was a great improvement on the humble portable electric drill and stand. Having got these machines installed, and demonstrated his own skill at metal turning and tool-sharpening, he duly declared that what the group must now have was a skilled mechanic. But not just any old mechanic; he must have Russel Aves (who was, he said, wasted in his present group), and Russel Aves he got.

Russel had been senior laboratory assistant at the Cavendish Lab. Starting there at the time when Lord Rutherford was Cavendish professor, he became the personal assistant to Sir Lawrence Bragg, Rutherford's successor. Skilled in all the classical laboratory techniques, they did not come better than Russ Aves.

The fact that everyone at Leeson House was crowded in as on a refugee ship seemed to have little adverse effect on the work. Typically with scientists, provided there were adequate supplies of electric power and tea there were few complaints. As I recollect, tea was not a problem!

Providing adequate supplies of electricity was, however, the greatest problem for the site engineers, since with valve equipment each experimenter could easily account for a half to one kilowatt. Most of the wiring for lab power points was run from room to room in the form of individual stout insulated conductors supported on porcelain insulators, rather than the usual multi-core cables. It was not unusual for these conductors to be running noticeably warm.

The heavy loading meant that the voltage was generally well below the nominal 230 volts (which was then the most common supply voltage). Fortunately there was a handy device called a Variac. This was a variable mains transformer normally intended to vary the mains voltage continuously from zero to its maximum. By connecting them in reverse, a supply which had dropped to 190 volts for example, could be raised back to its original 230 volts. These useful devices were in great demand and in wide use. Occasionally, forgetting that a particular Variac was wired in reverse, someone would smartly turn the dial back towards its zero end with rather spectacular results!

Within a short distance of the stables was an ideal place for the trailers containing the 10 centimetre sets. The large field bordered by the Swanage–Langton road dropped away from the high ground giving a clear view over Swanage Bay to the Isle of Wight. Many days the Needles, some nineteen miles distant, were visible, and when it was particularly clear one could see St Catherine's Head thirty-two miles away.

A mains supply for the trailers was run out to the field from the stables and Jimmy Atkinson set to work to see what results could be obtained from our 10 centimetre equipment. Swanage town provided a good array of echoes. Particularly useful in this respect was Oldfield School, a conspicuous red-brick building which stood proudly alone on its own small hill and was hence easily identified among the received signals at a range of one and a half miles.

Day after day Jimmy would work away to improve gradually the received signals by patiently determining the optimum working conditions for the magnetron and Sutton tube, whilst at the same time making constant tuning adjustments to the various parts of the set.

Concurrently, Skinner, Burcham, Ward and others were busy in the lab, continually improving the ancillary items such as crystal mixers, aerial-matching stubs and the like, all of which were fashioned principally out of short lengths of brass tubing soldered together, a process which was light-heartedly referred to as 'plumbing'. As each item was ready for test it would be fitted into the set in the trailer by Jimmy who would make comparative tests.

By degrees, the echoes on Jimmy's cathode-ray tube became stronger. Then one day a ghost signal was noticed, not directly on the tube trace but faintly in the background. It was in fact beyond the normal range of the timebase which had been set at ten miles on what is known as the 'flyback'. Extending the timebase, the small group of echoes came into view at a range equivalent to about twenty miles. To everyone's excitement it was realized that those echoes were from the Needles.

From this moment on there was no looking back, and as one improved component followed another the range of reception increased until the hitherto undreamt of target was reached – St Catherine's Head at about thirty-two miles.

All the elements of a basic system were now performing efficiently with one exception – the means of linking transmitter and receiver into a common aerial with a single parabolic mirror. This was going to be essential for the AI application in which the scanning aerial was to be accommodated within a perspex nose-cone on the twin-engined aircraft to be used.

Various methods were considered and tried by 'the plumbers', without producing a system which did not suffer an unacceptable loss of power. It would be almost the following summer before a satisfactory solution was found by A.H. Cooke at Oxford University. It was a device called a TR cell which cleverly combined a spark gap with a resonant cavity. The latter was that used in the reflecting klystron and hence the device became known as a 'soft Sutton tube'.

At the time of each transmitter pulse (1,000 to 2,000 times per second), the discharge across the gap effectively blocked the feed to the receiver, preventing it from becoming paralysed by the powerful magnetron pulse. What had made the design difficult was the need to ensure that the cell recovered within a few millionths of a second following the cessation of each transmitted pulse, hence allowing the receiver to function.

While the basic centimetre technology was being perfected Lovell and Hodgkin set about devising a possible AI system to be known as AI Mark VII. Once a prototype had been built and successfully tested, production could be put in hand by GEC. The new Bristol Beaufighter had been selected as the aircraft type to be equipped with the new system, but first its effectiveness must be proved by flight trials. Accordingly Blenheim N3522 had been allocated for this purpose. The Blenheim, like the Beaufighter designed to succeed it, was a light twin-engined fighter/bomber. Already this type had been used as a night-fighter equipped with 1½ metre AI with which Lovell had had some experience. To design a centimetre system to fit the confines of such aircraft presented a major challenge.

The parabolic aerial assembly would be accommodated within a perspex extension to the nose of the aircraft. But having, as intended, produced a radar with a narrow beam to avoid the obtrusive ground returns which nullified the effectiveness of the broad-beam 1½ metre systems, to cover a useful field of search the centimetre beam must be moved around in some ordered pattern.

It was here that Hodgkin displayed a unique ability in creative design. He devised a spiral scanning pattern associated with which was a radial display which was as clever in conception as it was straightforward for aircrews to assimilate. The design and production of the scanner was entrusted to Messrs Nash and Thompson of Tolworth, Surrey, whose pedigree originated with Frazer Nash, a famous pre-war motor-racing driver. They were acknowledged experts in hydraulics, and their most outstanding product had been hydraulic multiple gun-turrets which were fitted to RAF bombers, giving them the sharpest teeth of any air arm of the day.

The original scanner was hence hydraulically driven although later there would be an electrical version. A rotating mirror was made to change its angle of inclination during the course of several revolutions from its normal central position to an angle of 45 degrees, from which it would similarly return to repeat the next cycle. The path traced by the beam was hence a spiral, and it was so arranged that the forward path interlaced with its return. The width of the beam was nominally 10 degrees.

The practical manifestation of this principle was a 28-inch diameter aluminium dish being whirled around at some sixteen revolutions per second, a complete cycle being accomplished in little more than a second. To see the scanner operating on its test frame was a most alarming experience. Fortunately there is no recorded case of anyone being decapitated by one of these flying mirrors!

The associated display which Alan Hodgkin devised presented a picture in which a target located directly ahead would appear as a circle, the radius of which represented the distance from the fighter plane. A 'bandit' which, for example, was at nine o'clock to the searching fighter, would appear as a small segment of arc at a corresponding position on the display. As the pilot headed towards his prey the arc would open out to form a complete circle as the fighter became lined up with the target. Assuming that he was able to overtake the enemy, the circle on the display would gradually decrease in diameter as the distance between the two aircraft was reduced.

The block of echoes inevitably received back from the ground which had been such a disadvantage in the 1½ metre systems was to provide a useful additional feature in the centimetre version. These responses would appear as a straight line across the lower half of the display, where they would function as an artificial horizon. The line would be horizontal while the plane was in level flight, tipping to one side or the other as the aircraft banked. Furthermore, the line would rise as the pilot put the plane's nose down and would descend as the machine went into a climb.

All this information was, of course, directly available to the pilot from the plane's instruments, but it was discovered that it was of help to the radar operator to know how much the pilot had banked and otherwise responded to his instructions when making an interception. It can be appreciated that with all this information presented on a single radar screen it was immediately popular with the aircrews. In fact with this unique presentation Hodgkin had a winner.

Once the airborne units started to take shape under Lovell's guidance based on his experience of 1½ metre AI, it soon became apparent how the bulky apparatus of our early experiments could be transformed into compact equipment able to be flown. The secret lay mainly in the aircraft power supplies which unlike the public alternating current supply generated at a frequency of 50 hertz, was at a frequency of some 1,600 hertz. Since the physical size of power-supply components such as transformers, chokes and capacitors is inversely proportional to the frequency of the supply, those used in airborne equipment were fortuitously twenty to thirty times smaller than their ground-based equivalents.

In order to develop and test airborne units, suitable generator sets were made up for us. They consisted of an aircraft generator mounted on a board and driven by an electric motor connected to the public supply. Like most machinery of this nature it could be noisy, particularly the generator, which operated at a frequency well within the musical scale, and we had at least two of these sets running at any one time.

Fortunately there was a pair of chicken hutches at the rear of the stables. They were adequately weatherproof and apart from the necessity to crawl in on hands and knees when adjustments were required they were ideal to house our generators. But I imagine Joe Airey the site engineer raised his eyebrows when he received a requisition for his electricians to install a 415 volt, three-phase mains supply in two hen-houses!

9 Clandestine Visits

It was on 31 August 1940, about the time that the move to Leeson House was underway, that the *Duchess of Richmond* sailed for Halifax, Nova Scotia, with a very important party on board. This was the Tizard Mission which was ultimately bound for the United States with the object of soliciting technological help from the USA and Canada. The utmost secrecy was necessary, not only because the party carried with them information concerning Britain's latest scientific devices and a number of samples including the precious magnetron, but because the United States at that time was maintaining a neutral stance.

A remarkable covert friendship had been established between Premier Churchill and President Roosevelt, who was anxious to help Britain resist the Nazis, but had to tread warily. The American people in general and Congress in particular had no desire at that time to become involved in Europe's conflicts; they were only just recovering from the effects of the great depression. But Roosevelt had the foresight of a born statesman and could see the way the winds of war were likely to blow. In answer to Churchill's plea 'Give us the tools and we will finish the job', he took what measures his position as president allowed him, not only overtly but to a generous degree covertly.

The Tizard Mission was hence one facet, albeit a vital one, of this undercover co-operation. The party was not only of scientists, including Tizard himself, Cockcroft and Fowler (two senior Cavendish men), and Bowen (a Bawdsey 'old boy'), but representatives of the three services, namely Colonel F.C.

Wallace, a Dunkirk survivor; Captain H.W. Faulkner, RN; and Group Captain Pearce from RAF Coastal Command. Woodward Nutt was secretary. In Canada the Mission was joined by Dean Mackenzie and Air Vice Marshall Steadman. Incidently, Fowler was already in Canada as a liaison man.

In selecting an integrated team of civilian scientists and service chiefs Tizard was following the pattern already established by A.P. Rowe. The resultant ability of the scientific civilians to expound and discuss strategic aspects of warfare, whilst the service chiefs could show a familiarity with scientific detail, made a very deep impression on the Americans who worked in distinct compartments to the extent that there was no liaison whatever between their Army and Navy. Quite to the contrary, the extent of their mutual isolation led them to spy on each other. It did not surprise us to learn that it was the US Navy who were the most successful at this ridiculous game of espionage.

Undoubtedly this compartmentalization was the major factor in the USA being light-years behind Great Britain in the vital new science of RDF. In terms of innovation and new developments it was Britain who was consistently to lead the way throughout the war. Where the Americans excelled, however, was in production. It was not just their seemingly limitless manufacturing capacity that was impressive but their flare for production design. So here fortuitously was an ideal combination: British ingenuity with American production ability.

This, therefore, was one tangible result of the Tizard Mission; yet another was the establishment of an American equivalent of TRE. This was the Radiation Laboratory which was set up as MIT (Massachusetts Institute of Technology) at Boston, and where Dr Bowen was to spend much of his time during the succeeding years of the war.

The high spot of the Mission's tour, however, took place quietly on Sunday 6 October at the famous Bell Laboratories. This was the first demonstration outside Britain of the new wonder magnetron. The awesome responsibility of safeguarding

Sir John Cockcroft

Lord Cherwell (F.A. Lindermann)

Sir Robert Watson-Watt

Sir Mark Oliphant

AMRE Worth Matravers, Dorset 1940

Leeson House, near Swanage. The stables can be seen at top right

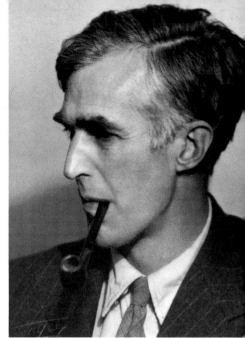

Prof. P.I. Dee (left)
with Sir Samuel
Curran

Prof. H.W.B. Skinner

Sir Bernard Lovell

Prof.W.E.Burcham

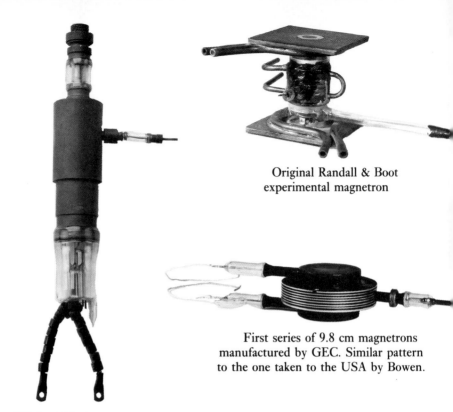

Oliphant klystron

Original Randall & Boot
experimental magnetron

First series of 9.8 cm magnetrons
manufactured by GEC. Similar pattern
to the one taken to the USA by Bowen.

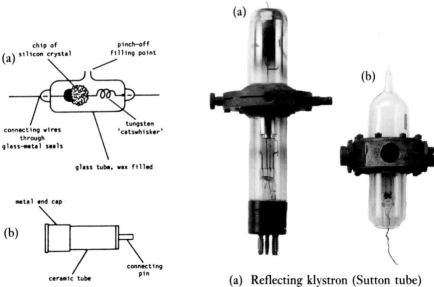

(a) chip of silicon crystal
pinch-off filling point
connecting wires through glass-metal seals
tungsten 'catswhisker'
glass tube, wax filled

(b) metal end cap
ceramic tube
connecting pin

(a) Skinner crystal
(b) Production version

(a) Reflecting klystron (Sutton tube)
(b) TR cell ('soft' Sutton tube)

S) EXP BEAUFIGHTER
SYSTEM (SCANNER)
MITTER AND MIXER
REMOVED

Spiral scanner of 9.8 cm A1
system. Version shown is electrical
type used on mk VIII

Sir Alan Hodgkin – creator
of the unique spiral scanning
system

Example of the spiral display. Inner ring
(transmitter pulse) represents zero range. Outer ring
indicates plane's altitude (4,000 ft in example). The
horizontal band is due to ground returns (echoes). It
conveniently functions as an artificial horizon. Arc to
left would be a target 20° off the fighter's heading
and at a range of 2 miles. As fighter heads towards
it, the arc will become a full circle and as the
pursued approaches, the diameter decreases

) EXP BEAUFIGHTER

FUSELAGE NOSE
PERSPEX)

Bristol Beaufighter
showing Perspex
fuselage nose which
houses the scanner

Lancaster bomber fitted with H$_2$S. Radar scanner housed in perspex cupola shown on underbelly of the aircraft.

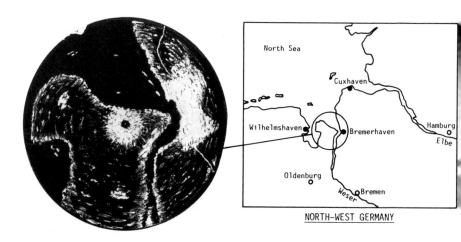

Typical display of 3 cm H$_2$S as would appear when flying over the area shown

TRE senior staff and visitors shown at a Sunday Soviet. Notable among the visitors were Sir Robert Renwick, Lord Cherwell and Air Vice Marshall Sir Victor Tait (front row, fourth, fifth and sixth from left respectively), and Wing Commander Derek Jackson (in civilian clothes, back row, last on right)

Superintendent A.P. Rowe with his senior staff. Left to right: J.R. Ratcliffe, R.A. Smith, C. Holt-Smith, R. Cockburn (standing), A.P. Rowe, W.B. Lewis

Malvern College grounds as seen from the Main Building. Centre
is the 'hallowed' Senior Turf whilst beyond is the canteen, main
stores, etc.

The Royal visit, July 1943. The presentation of the apprentices'
model scanner. Left to right: Sir Stafford Cripps (Minister of Aircraft
Production), 'Wally' Betteridge (foreman), Queen Elizabeth,
King George VI, Air Commodore Gregory (EU manager),
Lady Cripps. Joe Morley (chief foreman) is between and
immediately behind their majesties

this most secret device in its transport to America had been entrusted to Bowen. A select group of staff at Bell Laboratories had been briefed in advance as to what power supplies and associated equipment, including a suitable magnet, would be required for the demonstration.

As the distinguished party assembled, the precious valve was connected into the Bell set-up. A hush descended on the party as the equipment was switched on and the high-voltage supply slowly adjusted. Suddenly a bright glow-discharge appeared around the output stub as the magnetron burst into oscillation. A neon lamp held close by glowed brightly. The assembled company watched in amazement, just as we had done on that memorable July morning in our hut at Worth Matravers. 'Gee, you mean to say that's really 10 centimetres?' exclaimed one of the American scientists incredulously. A wavemeter was promptly brought in and the wavelength measured. As claimed by GEC who made it, it was 9.8 centimetres. But what impressed the Americans most was the amount of power this modest-sized device could produce – a thousand times (literally) that of the klystrons with which they themselves had been working.

This demonstration of the unique Randall/Boot magnetron – described in an official American account as 'the most valuable cargo ever brought to our shores' – brought the successful Tizard Mission to its conclusion. British/American co-operation in science and technology had been firmly cemented even though it had to be kept under wraps until the violence of Pearl Harbor brought the United States formally into the war in December 1941.

The Mission had also visited Canada, where arrangements were made for Canadian firms to produce versions of a number of established British radars, and to supplement British production of magnetrons and other specialized valves. Some of this work would be done in co-operation with the Radiation Laboratory, and Bowen was left behind to co-ordinate all these efforts.

The first fruits of the Tizard Mission were not long in

maturing. We were soon to receive some items of 10 centimetre 'plumbing' in the shape of experimental crystal-mixers, TR cells, and the like. They were duly put to the test, but compared to our own devices they were much inferior in performance. In general their techniques significantly lagged behind our own. Accordingly Skinner had a selection of our own parts sent back across the Atlantic with the gentle hint that they would do better to copy ours. Here was the start of the 'we design it, you build it' co-operation that was to have such a war-winning potential.

A further outcome of the Mission's work occurred one dull Saturday afternoon in November 1940. At the time we were not aware of the connection, for when a number of us in the group had been asked to attend for a VIP demonstration we were not told who was coming. Although Saturday was then the establishment's day off it was not unusual for demonstrations to be given outside normal working hours.

Having got the 10 centimetre set in the trailer working and lined up satisfactorily, we left it and assembled in the field outside, just as a motorcade made its way up the hilly Leeson House drive. The convoy did not proceed to the front of the house itself but took the turning straight towards our spot by the stables.

Expecting to see uniformed service chiefs or government ministers, we were taken aback to see, following Rowe and his staff out of the cars, what looked like four Chicago gangsters. This was because the secret visitors were dressed in long-jacketed lightish blue suits and broad-brimmed trilby hats which were then typical of American attire as seen in Hollywood films.

Someone quietly informed us that they were a party of US Army Generals and a US Navy Admiral. They were in mufti for security reasons but they would have been less conspicuous had they worn their uniforms!

The party stepped gingerly across the muddy corner of the field to reach the trailer, where they were greeted by Jimmy Atkinson, who was to make the demonstration. Right on time the target aircraft from Christchurch arrived to fly its pre-arranged course; meanwhile the rest of us stood quietly at a discreet distance keeping our fingers crossed.

Suddenly there was a loud bang like a pistol shot from the direction of the trailer ('Who said these guys weren't gangsters?' remarked some wag). Immediately the door of the trailer opened and out came the four Americans wearing broad smiles closely followed by Jimmy who announced that a 10,000 volt capacitor in the power unit had just blown up. It was fortunate that the demonstation was just drawing to a close and by that time the US Service Chiefs had been duly impressed. Doubtless by the time they were back home it was the exploding capacitor which left the greatest impression.

Joking apart, this confidential visit was to lead to the Americans' own development programme in 10 centimetre AI and GL equipments, but so carefully had the visit been arranged that neither the Swanage people nor indeed the rest of TRE were aware of what had taken place.

* * *

As the weeks went by the Luftwaffe increased the range and severity of their bombing. While the nightly raids on London were maintained all the other major cities across the land were visited in turn and repeatedly bombed. And so it was that this year of 1940, which came in with a whimper, reached its final end in terror and destruction. From the phoney war Britain had come to know the violence of total war.

With a modest sense of achievement the group gathered together for that last evening of 1940 as guests of Jimmy and Mona Atkinson to welcome in the New Year. As the last minutes of the old year ticked away we assembled in their candlelit dining room, our glasses charged with an excellent punch, to hear Jimmy propose the toast to 1941. He echoed the feelings of us all as he expressed the hope that the new year would bring the victory for which we all prayed.

As Big Ben sounded its majestic strokes of midnight over the radio we raised our glasses to the toast and the hope of that early victory, but we all knew in our innermost selves that there could be a long, hard struggle ahead.

10 Who Said Centimetres Were Not for This War?

The intensification of the night raids against all our major cities was a stark reminder of the necessity to press ahead with centimetre AI with all urgency. This was the implied message as we entered 1941. Before we could win the night air war against the Luftwaffe however, our group had to win the war with GEC. As soon as we had the unbeatable combination of the cavity magnetron and the reflecting klystron, all ideas of using GEC's 25 centimetre system evaporated, but they were not going to capitulate without a struggle.

The battle was now over the type of modulator to be used. The function of the modulator in radar is to turn on the transmitter (in our case the magnetron) for the short duration of a pulse by effectively switching its high-voltage supply. Our system developed by Jimmy Atkinson used a high-voltage valve to effect the switching. This was termed a 'hard valve modulator'. GEC on the other hand had favoured the use of a high-voltage thyratron – a form of gas discharge tube. Unfortunately this type was prone to a form of instability called 'jitter', whereas the hard valve, as well as being physically smaller, could produce a much sharper pulse.

Ironically the hard valve was a product of Marconi/Osram, Osram being a GEC subsidiary, whilst their pet thyratron was manufactured by Metropolitan Vickers. Nevertheless, a technical impasse developed between our two camps which was resolved only by running a contest between the two systems.

It was agreed that GEC and TRE should each engineer a set of prototype units ('boxes' in common parlance) with which comparative trials would be carried out at our site at Leeson.

For us to construct, wire up, and test a whole set of boxes by the appointed date meant burning a fair amount of midnight oil. Those of us involved would return to the lab after the evening meal and work through to any time between 2 a.m. and 6 a.m. We had in the preceeding months frequently worked such extended hours whenever it was required to accelerate the course of the works. We were all keen to see our centimetre radar into service, and for those of us in lodgings it was no hardship.

We customarily worked until 7 p.m. each day, so for these late night sessions we would return around 9 p.m. At midnight we would break off and brew up some tea. We would then sit around the well-stoked iron stove. Generally the conversation would relate to the progress of the work, but quite often it would be on some scientific subject which never failed to be interesting and at times memorable.

A popular subject was the further applications of centimetre radar, even extending to post-war uses. Jimmy Atkinson's favourite topic was the possibility of getting radar echoes from the moon which of course was a wayout idea in those days. One essential ingredient would be a sufficiently large dish for the aerial. His projected solution was to excavate a parabolic-shaped bowl 100 feet in diameter in the ground using a bulldozer. It would then be lined with concrete and covered with wire netting to provide a metallic reflective surface. Jimmy would expound these ideas with a twinkle in his eye and few of us took him seriously; nevertheless, there is at least one radio telescope in the world which has since been constructed on these lines.

It was hardly surprising therefore that the world's first radio telescope was the brainchild of a member of our late-night tea sessions – Bernard Lovell. Lovell's Jodrell Bank telescope, however, needed to be steerable, which demanded superhuman efforts in the construction and financing of the unique giant structure which was to make world history.

In due course the appointed week for comparative trials was with us, and the GEC team arrived with their equipment. They made themselves busy installing it in a trailer which we had provided alongside our own. There was little contact between our two teams, in fact the GEC party would make their appearance only at meal times. After about three days the suspense was more than Jimmy and Skinner could bear and I was sent out to their trailer on some pretext or other with the object of taking a quick look at anything which might be in operation. They were not going to fall for that one, and I returned with nothing to report. Next I was sent out after dark with the ubiquitous neon lamp with which to check whether any power was issuing from their aerial. I crept quietly towards the aerial dish which stood close by their trailer and held the lamp near to the aerial elements. It glowed only faintly which delighted Jimmy and Skinner when I reported back. It seemed that their power was well down on ours. Before the week was out they were getting some reasonable results, but when all the various factors were considered it was the TRE system which was adopted.

Ironically, neither modulator system survived for very long as within the following year an alternative method was developed by Sam Curran. This used a triggered spark gap as a high-voltage switch and an artificial section of transmission line (called a delay line) which determined the duration and shape of the pulse. It was engineered and put into quantity production by Metropolitan Vickers of Manchester and became the standard unit for many systems including H_2S.

It was not only the GEC team who were given to working behind closed doors, for very soon we were to give house-room to a party of gentlemen for whom confidentiality was a way of life. They were, after all, connected with the 'silent service' – the Royal Navy.

During the summer of 1940 when we were exciting the top brass of both the RAF and the Army with our demonstration of 10 centimetre radar, the Admiralty appeared to show no interest, even though the final breakthrough had been made thanks to the two Admiralty scientists who had come up with their reflecting klystron. The Navy, it seemed, were firmly wedded to their 50 centimetre systems.

Britain was facing a situation as grave as the blitz, which Churchill, with his brilliance at coining phrases, called 'the Battle of the Atlantic'. Vital supplies of food, oil, munitions, and so on were having to be brought across the Atlantic. The convoys of supply ships were being seriously threatened by the German U-boat packs.

Ironically, the one person in the Admiralty who sensed the value of 10 centimetre radar for detecting U-boats was the chief of our own submarine fleet, Admiral Horton. For him we staged a special demonstration from our trailer in the grounds of Leeson House late in 1940. He arrived complete, in a manner of speaking, with one of his own submarines.

Little did the worthy inhabitants of Swanage know that on this particular day a submarine had been circling around the bay. It showed no more than its conning tower, which was all that was needed for the test, so as to ensure the strict secrecy of the operation.

The demonstration was very successful, for we obtained good echoes from the small portions of the vessel which were above the surface during its several circuits of the bay. The Admiral was very impressed and departed a happy man. Then it all went quiet again for some weeks until we were told that a team of four Admiralty scientists were to descend upon us to learn about 10 centimetres.

They were men of few words who took everything seriously. They allowed themselves little time for socializing, and set about the task of assimilating all the details of our equipment and putting together a basic set with due despatch. As well as technical data we provided them with an empty trailer and all the bits and pieces required for the construction of a complete 10 centimetre set.

All this occupied several weeks and when it came to getting results from the equipment these Admiralty people were hardly more communicative than the GEC team – at least the latter had good reason since they were upholding the confidentiality of a rival system. Nevertheless, the time came when the Admiralty team leader declared his satisfaction with the results they had obtained and so a towing vehicle was duly ordered and the trailer, complete with its precious cargo, closely followed by its four silent custodians, disappeared from our domain.

No further thought was given to these individuals until a few months later when supplies of magnetrons, modulator valves and in particular the special valveholders for the latter, which were only obtainable from the USA, suddenly became short. It was discovered that it was the Admiralty who were cornering our hitherto exclusive market.

It transpired that the Navy team's trailer had been towed to the Admiralty labs at Eastney, near Portsmouth, from where it was loaded in its entirety on to a ship for sea trials. So successful were the trials that a contract was immediately placed with the Allen West company of Brighton to manufacture a hundred sets – hence our component shortages. At the same time a dozen pre-production models were constructed at the Eastney labs in order to get these sets (Type 271) into service as soon as possible. By August 1941 twenty-five corvettes were equipped and ready to go to sea. It was ironic that the Navy, which was the last service to consider 10 centimetre radar, was the first to have a 10 centimetre system operational.

As for our own AI project, the controversy with GEC regarding the details of the system having been resolved amicably as a result of the comparative trials, construction of a set of units for installation in the Blenheim had begun in earnest. By April of that year the first set was ready for flight trials to commence.

The trials were immediately successful, although not conducted without hazard. Alan Hodgkin, who made some of the test flights, was somewhat alarmed on one occasion when, having asked the pilot where they were, he was told that they were over the Channel Islands! Tragedy really struck, however, when Downing – one of Hodgkin's team – lost his life when his plane was shot down. Ironically, it was a Spitfire pilot who mistook the plane for a German bomber.

Following the initial trials, further flights were made by experienced night-fighter pilots and observers who reacted favourably to the system's performance and to the novel form of display. A manufacturing programme was put in hand consisting of twelve pre-production models for training purposes which were built during the autumn of 1941, followed by a hundred production equipments.

Although it was not until early in 1942 that the system became operational, just as the German bombing offensive was in decline, nevertheless the four Beaufighter squadrons accounted for some hundred 'kills' within the first nine months of AI Mark VII operation.

Concurrently with the pre-production phase of the Mark VII programme, J.A. Ratcliffe and his training organization arrived from Petersham to do for the RAF with the new AI Mark VII what they had been doing for the army with their gun-laying radar. Forres School building in Swanage was duly requisitioned to provide accommodation for this new division of TRE. Very soon they were to develop into a wide-ranging organization covering all the new systems as they were introduced into the RAF. The division was staffed mainly by an influx of graduates from Hankey courses – degree courses run on a compressed timescale and named after Lord Hankey, the government minister who introduced them. Their work embraced commissioning, training service personnel, feeding back operational experience to the design groups, and design of special test equipment. All this came under the title of 'Post Design Services' or PDS, a feature adopted by many organizations after the war.

Let it not be thought that by now the project had become institutionalized and our work stuck into a mundane groove, for by 1941 applications of centimetre technique began to proliferate and likewise the numbers of those engaged in it.

Following on the heels of our Admiralty colleagues came two well-dressed (by our wartime standards) gentlemen with a large van-load of equipment packed in crates. With the help of Alan Edmunds and myself they proceeded to unload them.

Two things caught our attention. The younger of the two, a smart, well-bred young man, had slipped off the jacket of his well-cut light grey suit while he took his part in the unloading, thereby displaying a pair of transparent plastic braces, the like of which we had never seen before. The other point of interest was that they both had American accents.

Heath and Corsen, who were to spend about six months with us, were from the new Radiation Laboratory of the Massachusetts Institute of Technology, which had been set up following the Tizard Mission to North America. In hardly six months of its existence the laboratory had produced a version of a centimetre AI system to a programme negotiated by Dr Bowen and using British-inspired 10 centimetre components. This version was to use the more straightforward helical scanner, but it required a twin cathode-ray tube display to impart the three parameters of range, azimuth and elevation. Hodgkin's unique spiral display embodied all three in a single-tube display, but the spiral scanner was somewhat more complicated. Here, then, in these packing cases were the results of MIT's work which with Heath and Corsen (and a twin-engined aircraft in which to fly the system) had faced the hazards of an Atlantic convoy in order that comparative tests could be made with our own system.

Edmunds and myself had been detailed to provide whatever assistance and material the two transatlantic visitors required. We found this no hardship since they were both friendly and outgoing. Heath, the senior of the two, was the more practical, presumably being an engineer by profession. He was tall and well built so that one could imagine he had played football for Yale or Harvard, but for the fact that he was a Canadian. Corsen, of quieter demeanour, was a well-qualified physicist and was impatiently conscientious in his work. He was cultured and well groomed, and was never seen other than wearing a well-laundered shirt and sober tie.

It was fascinating to see their equipment, which we recognized from American radio publications as being typical. The principal difference between British and American units was the multiplicity of valves ('tubes' in their parlance). Here in Britain valves were significantly more expensive due to taxation and royalties, compared with America's economy of scale. Traditionally, therefore, our circuits had to be more highly developed and efficient. A particular circuit function which might, for example, be accomplished using a pair of pentode valves would unashamedly be performed by the Americans using twice the quantity of double-triodes. As in automobile engineering, so with electronics.

The modulator in the MIT equipment used four high-voltage valves in parallel connection, whilst within the glass envelope of each were four separate electrode assemblies strapped together. The heater supply power for this bank was considerable and produced much heat. Our modulator used a single transmitting-type valve, the copper anode of which was integral with the glass to which it was sealed to form the envelope. By this configuration the cooling fins could be fitted in direct contact with the anode. Although the American array was no match for the efficiency of ours, nevertheless as a product each of these multiple-electrode valves was sheer beauty to behold.

The aircraft that had been shipped over and given into the caring hands of the Experimental Flying Unit at Christchurch was a twin-engined commercial airliner – a Boeing 247D. The accommodation was first class (as was passenger flight before the war), for down each side of the cabin was a row of comfortable seats like armchairs. There would have been a total of about sixteen of these, but all those along one side had been removed and in their place had been fitted a long bench with numerous power supply points (115 volts, 400 hertz in their case) for the radar equipment. In addition there were 24-volt DC sockets for their miniature low-voltage soldering iron. This latter facility really impressed us for such irons had not been seen in Britain at that time. With all these unique facilities the aircraft was a veritable flying laboratory in which repairs and modifications could be made while in flight.

The results with the MIT system were, broadly speaking, comparable to our own although not as efficient as the TRE version; nor at the outset was their receiver as sensitive. However, these side-by-side trials of the two systems provided valuable experience for the MIT team. This led to the development of the American SCR 720 AI sets, which were put into large-scale production in the States. Although Hodgkin's single-tube display was preferred to the American's twin-tube presentation, it was considered that this display and the helical scanner would offer greater immunity from enemy countermeasures – an eventuality never proved. Nevertheless, the SCR 720 was adopted by the RAF as standard towards the end of the war, becoming designated as AI Mark X. Meanwhile the RAF's Mark VII and the uprated Mark VIII, which was to follow, were to operate with considerable success even though the intensity of the Luftwaffe's night bombing was to decline after 1942.

When Heath and Corsen returned to America they took only the key items of their equipment since crossing the Atlantic in wartime was no Sunday outing. Our group found their tools and spares very welcome in the lab but the star prize was the Boeing aircraft. Henceforth the group were the enviable possessors of this remarkable and comfortable flying lab which was invaluable for flight-testing a whole variety of experimental equipment.

11 Centimetre Technology Expands

As the year advanced, 10 centimetre techniques having become well established, basic work had been put in train to explore the feasibility of even shorter wavelengths. It appeared that 3 centimetres was now practical and soon the first models of a 3 centimetre magnetron were in our possession. Initially they were water-cooled and had been made by BTH of Rugby, who had been brought into the business in order to broaden the country's development and supply capability in this increasingly important field of technology.

This new avenue of exploration was principally the concern of Jimmy Atkinson and Skinner, while Dee continued to be responsible for all 10 centimetre developments. Another GL trailer was obtained and lined up alongside that occupied by the original 10 centimetre equipment, which was still a very important test bed. Although improved coaxial cables were now available it was apparent from calculation that at a third of the wavelength the losses were going to be intolerable. At 3 centimetres the use of waveguides to connect the aerial to the transmitter/receiver complex was going to be essential.

The first waveguide assembly was somewhat basic, for the theory of the various modes of transmission was complex and had yet to be studied and mastered. Much of this work was in due course to be the responsibility of a bright young physicist by the name of John Adams, who took to the subject with alacrity. He was destined to go far, which indeed he did. In the post-war world of science he flourished to become Director of CERN, the international centre of high-energy physics at Geneva.

Initially a tubular waveguide assembly was constructed by Russel Aves using brass tubing of appropriate diameter. This first simple system had one serious disadvantage. The whole assembly, including magnetron, a heavy electro-magnet, receiver mixer, TR network, aerial feeder, and the aerial itself with an 18-inch diameter mirror was necessarily a single rigid unit mounted on a wooden baseboard. Rotating waveguide joints and flexible sections were to be developed eventually but in the meantime the weighty baseboard had to be moved around in order to train the aerial on to a target. This was impractical for any purpose other than initial setting-up and so the baseboard assembly was placed in front of one of the two opening flaps of the trailer, lined up on the Needles and with the aid of wood blocks given a small degree of elevation.

In order to conduct tests with a target aircraft, the radar tail had to wag the aeronautical dog. In other words, the aircraft was obliged to fly backwards and forwards between us and the Isle of Wight at as low an altitude as permissible by which means the plane would be within the beam over most of the distance. This procedure worked remarkably well until the day Sir Sholto Douglas visited TRE following his appointment as AOC in C, Fighter Command. As usual, centimetres were the last of the items on the demonstration programme, which inevitably overran. No matter – our aircraft was still on its back-and-forth runs through centimetre alley (as this strip was now called) as the VIPs arrived, and we gave a convincing demonstration. Next door to us was the very latest in radar technology – the lock-follow system, brainchild of Dr F.C. Williams. A 10 centimetre scanner under the control of the electronics was designed to search for a target and when found, to lock on to it. The centimetre equipment had been designed and provided by Lovell in close co-operation. The system was in its early stages, however, and had been made initially to operate in only one plane – azimuth. Hence for the demonstration the Lovell/ Williams partnership required the target aircraft to fly crossways. Unfortunately, when the time came for the plane to change course by 90 degrees communication had broken down

– it continued its inwards and outwards course. All that the AOC in C could see of this latest marvel of technology therefore was a buzzing, schizophrenic robot!

* * *

Progress had not stood still with 10 centimetre magnetrons however. The standard 9.8 centimetre model as manufactured by GEC had been significantly improved in both stability and output efficiency by the technique of 'strapping.' This apparently simple idea of linking alternate cavities by wire straps was the result of an inspired analysis of the *modus operandi* of the cavity magnetron by J. Sayers of the Oliphant team. Strangely, the purpose of strapping completely baffled the Germans when they examined magnetrons from crashed RAF bombers.

The other significant development was the high-power version of the 10 centimetre genre. By scaling up physically and using a more powerful magnet with a proportionately higher working voltage, the power output had been raised some ten times.

The evolution of the high-power magnetron was opportune. There was already the need for a long-range radar capable of accurate range and bearing measurement, and one largely immune from possible enemy jamming. These requirements were for GCI (Ground Controlled Interception) which provided sector control of night-fighters. Currently 1½ metre equipment was being used for this purpose but if ever there was a solution looking for a problem this was it. And so CMH (Centimetre Height Finding) was born.

To develop this new system a companion group was formed under the leadership of Dr John Warren, and a development contract was placed on BTH of Rugby, who would manufacture a number of operational sets. Everything about the project would be big, particularly the aerial, which would use a six-foot parabolic mirror to produce an exceptionally narrow beam.

The need to have a suitable site for the six-foot CMH mirror led to the Warren group being given the best of the accommodation in Leeson House. This was the lounge, which being at the front of the house had a commanding view out over Swanage Bay. To house the giant aerial system a conservatory was built out in front of the lounge french windows. To avoid any loss of power due to absorption at microwave frequencies, perspex was used in place of glass. The priceless panelling and carvings in the lounge had been boarded up and were in no danger from the incursion of the heavy equipment, although it was necessary to have some additional strong flooring laid over the original boards to support its weight.

The lounge, together with the rest of the house, was restored to its original state after the war, when it reverted to its pre-war function as a school. That was with the exception of a particular feature which graced the entrance hall. It was a carved wooden lion rampant which had crowned one of the newel posts of the Jacobean oak staircase. Mysteriously it had gone 'walkabout'; some say it found its way across the Atlantic!

CMH was just one more of the burgeoning applications of the centimetre technique. Around this time Jimmy proudly told me one morning that expenditure on centimetres to date had reached a million pounds. That figure now seems chicken-feed but in 1941 prices it amounted to no less than 8,000 Morris 8 motor cars – the Morris 8 being a handy currency equivalent which I used in those days.

This technological mushrooming was not exclusive to our own small world of centimetres. All groups at TRE were finding or creating new and original applications of their own particular brand of the radar art, as well as having to devise solutions at short notice to problems thrown up by the course of the war. Hence there was continuous expansion and ever-pressing demands for space to accommodate the regular intake of new staff and service personnel on attachment.

At the time of the occupation of Leeson House in the autumn of 1940 every inch of space was taken up. In less than a year the situation had therefore reached crisis proportions and the search was on for additional premises. Yet another prep school building was found and duly requisitioned. This was the large and rambling Durnford School not far up the hill from Leeson House, mid-way through the ancient linear village of Langton Matravers. Here it was within a not unreasonable walking distance, which some of us would traverse at lunchtime, for Durnford at least had the space and facility for a canteen.

The building was a rabbit warren of narrow corridors and staircases which led from one wing to another, one floor to another, with the odd side step to a mezzanine floor where least expected. On one of these floors (surprisingly not the ground floor) one came across an indoor swimming bath. Although full of water it looked far from inviting. In fact very little about this rather run-down edifice was inviting. Although Leeson House was probably at least a century older than Durnford it had a warmth and maturity which its cavernous neighbour certainly lacked.

About twelve months later, when TRE was moved out of Dorset, it was planned for the army to occupy Durnford in our place. It did not pass their inspection however, and they declined to take it on for billeting troops. Superintendent Rowe was later to declare proudly that his scientists worked without complaint in a building condemned by the army.

We had all become so used to shaking down anywhere, provided there was a mains supply and space for a bench, that we had become immunized against poor conditions. In any case we were only too aware how much easier life was for the likes of us compared to those in a wadi in the Western Desert or on an Atlantic convoy. Nonetheless, it was perhaps significant that the building was demolished after the war.

The doubtful surroundings were no bar to our happily taking lunch there. In fact the dining room, which had a pleasant outlook, was probably the best room in the place, though what the kitchens were like I fear to think.

A feature of these lunches was that Rowe to his credit did not run a captain's table (unless of course he was entertaining important visitors). He would choose a table at random where there was a place, and would hold a conversation with whoever was already seated.

It was several months following the German invasion of Soviet Russia when it happened that Rowe chose to join our own table. Lord Beaverbrook at Churchill's request had made a mission to Moscow to solicit what material and scientific help the new-found ally required. The outcome of this mission was of grave concern to Rowe. 'I am most worried,' he said, as he immediately brought up this subject.

He told us that Beaverbrook had brought back a long list of equipment and technical information that the Russians were requesting. What was worrying Rowe was the fact that the Soviets were offering no reciprocal information. 'We do not know whether they have any RDF, nor do we know of anything scientific they may have been working on, yet they expect us to tell all. It worries me no end.' I never forgot this conversation and it was to condition our attitude to this so-called ally four years later.

This expansion was not confined to TRE itself but also extended to its peripheral organizations. The Telecommunications Flying Unit, which provided our target aircraft and conducted flight trials, had long outgrown the space and facilities at Christchurch. This problem was solved by the construction of a new purpose-built airfield at Hurn, north of Bournemouth, which was opened in August. It survived after the war to become Bournemouth Airport.

At the same time a factory building was erected at West Howe, a northern suburb of Bournemouth, to provide TRE with its own production unit. Known as RPU, it was intended to handle short pre-production runs of urgently needed equipment. Supplemented by Ratcliffe's PDS organization, it provided a means of getting new systems into service with the RAF with the minimum of delay. Like Hurn airport the premises themselves have continued their existence to this day. The present occupier is British Telecom.

12 H₂S – Too Secret to Fly?

As the autumn of 1941 gave way to winter an important new development took place, so important that it came about under a new and tighter order of security.

Hitherto we had all worked together, enjoying an unrestricted interchange of information between groups and between individual scientific personnel. This was the principle established by Rowe following his belief that nothing was more conducive to rapid and successful scientific development than a free exchange of ideas and information between workers.

Developments had been taking place rapidly, not only in the field of centimetre radar, but across the whole range of the establishment's work, and at the same time staff numbers were increasing to the same degree. Under these circumstances the situation could easily get out of hand with a vital loss of security.

Ironically it was in July 1941 that the government chose to publicize the existence of RDF, albeit in very broad terms. To give members of the general public an instant understanding of what the new science was designed to do, the word 'Radiolocation' was coined, but later the less cumbersome term 'Radar', adopted by the Americans, came into general use and has remained as the accepted term internationally.

One of the first applications of the new internal security policy was within our own group. The wall of silence wasn't just thrown around the group, it was erected straight down the middle.

The first intimation we had of this new alien regime was one morning when Jimmy took Alan Edmunds and myself quietly on one side and told us to ignore any talk we might hear of 'Land ASV', and if we did hear anything, not to repeat it.

That was his bold instruction, with no explanation as to what it might be about; so when a few days later the group was quietly split in two, our half as before under Jimmy and Skinner, the remainder under Dee to embark on some mysterious project (Land ASV ?), Alan and I just had to find out.

The large lab next to our end room in the stables was given over to the new project. Here our erstwhile friends and colleagues sat quietly working away, keeping cards close to their corporate chests.

One was the young, hard-working junior scientific officer, J.V. Jelley. He was a meticulous and productive worker and he had been busy developing some new electronic circuits, all details of which we knew by his nature would have been carefully written up in his lab notebook. Taking advantage of a vacated lab one lunch period to indulge in a little espionage, we took a look at this notebook.

Our John Jelley was not only conscientious in his work but also in regard to security, for the manner in which he had compiled his notes gave us no clue as to the purpose of the circuits described. It was no wonder, therefore, that he had not found it necessary to conceal his notebook before leaving the lab. The only clue we had was a heading, 'BN Project'.

We set about the task of deciphering the initials 'BN'. This did not prove too difficult, remembering Jimmy's warning about 'Land ASV'. ASV, standing for Air to Surface Vessel, was an airborne radar application for detecting enemy ships (hopefully including U Boats) at sea. At that time it operated on 1½ metres but developments were in hand for a 10 centimetre version.

Conceivably a centimetre version, on account of its superior resolution, if flown over land rather than the sea, it would reveal major features of the topography below.

We made a connection between this thought and one of Air Chief Marshal Sir Phillip Joubert's regular pep talks at TRE. He had made a plea for some system of navigation for bombers which did not depend upon radio contact with ground stations and hence would not be restricted in range. So, did 'BN' stand for Bomber Navigation?

As the weeks went by we discovered that our thinking had been on the right lines.[1] We learnt that Dr Curran's associate Hensby had been engaged on flight trials in a Blenheim with a 10 centimetre AI set suitably modified to assess the possibility of a centimetre ASV system.

One of the test flights was planned to take place over the Bristol Channel in co-operation with a naval vessel, but the test proved abortive. It was reported that Hensby was frustrated and annoyed, valuable time having been wasted. In instructing the pilot to return for home he did not bother to switch the experimental set off.

A while later he was brought back from his thoughts by a sudden realization that a great splodge of light representing a whole mass of echoes was working its way slowly across the display tube as the aircraft made its way homeward. Unmistakable was the outline of the Severn estuary but the most prominent mass of illumination on his display tube he reasoned must be a built-up area.

A few minutes later they were flying over Chepstow!

From such an experience was born the latest application of centimetre radar, an innovation which if not altering the course of the war certainly enhanced the capabilities of Bomber Command to inflict a heavy toll on the enemy. Significantly this was at a time when the new super-heavy bombers – the Lancasters and Halifaxes – which possessed range and load-carrying capabilities hitherto not dreamt of, were coming into service.

This, then, was the mystery engaging Dee's half of the original centimetre group. It was allocated the code name H_2S and for a number of reasons it was considered absolutely vital that not a hint of such a system should reach the enemy.

Latterly there have been a number of claimants for the idea, but according to Lovell it came as a progression of thought from the earliest days of airborne radar experiments prior to the war. Since Lovell was intimately concerned from the beginning and was in charge of H_2S development from its start as a project, one must accept his as being the authoritative version. But for my own money I like to think that it was Hensby's experience over the Bristol Channel which was responsible for the idea taking off; a view shared with colleagues at the time.

As soon as it became evident that H_2S was likely to work, Bomber Command welcomed it with alacrity. So convinced were the authorities of its value in increasing the effectiveness of the bombing offensive that it was given the highest priority. Here at last was a navigational aid which would enable the RAF to locate and bomb a variety of important targets for practical reasons hitherto out of range; not least among these was Berlin. It was therefore hardly surprising that Churchill himself took an interest in its progress, which meant that Professor Lindemann, who the previous July had become Lord Cherwell, would take up a watching brief on the Prime Minister's behalf.

The work had hardly begun when Dee was obliged to attend a high-powered progress meeting at the Air Ministry. The meeting was not over-impressed by the extent of progress as reported by Dee. Cherwell in particular was most critical. In his defence Dee explained the difficulties they were working under – the need for more staff and more space in which to accommodate them.

'How much space do you think you need Mr Dee?' enquired an important-looking gentleman from the far end of the conference table. Caught a little off balance by the sudden direct question, Dee shrugged his shoulders and replied vaguely that something like a sixty-foot hut would do.

As Jimmy Atkinson put it some days later when quite unexpectedly a large lorry arrived loaded with wooden hut sections: 'That certainly was a *very* high-powered meeting.'

In a very short time brick footings were built in the field near our trailers upon which the hut was erected – all sixty-foot of it. As soon as the building was completed, benches erected, and services laid on, a squad of RAF radar mechanics arrived led by a Flight Sergeant. They immediately started work constructing a set of prototype units for flight trials. It certainly was a very high-powered meeting.

A pair of Halifax bombers were made available for experimental installations, each fitted with a perspex cupola beneath the fuselage to accommodate a scanning aerial. Concurrently a team was busy designing a centimetre aerial system which as well as having a narrow beam in the horizontal plane produced a broad distribution in the vertical.

The scanner would have a continuous 360-degree rotation and the cathode-ray tube display would have a trace which, originating from a centre point on the screen, would rotate in sympathy with the aerial. The received echoes recorded on the screen, which was to have a 'long afterglow', would produce a map-like presentation of the terrain over which the aircraft was flying, covering something like a ten to twenty mile radius.

This form of display is the now familiar Plan Position Indicator (PPI) which is used almost universally in marine and air-traffic control radars. In 1941 it was something of an innovation.

In little more than three months a prototype equipment had been designed, built, and installed in a Halifax ready for the flight trials, which took place in April 1942.

There was no doubt in the minds of those involved that H_2S as a system was going to work, but there was one serious obstacle which was to appear insurmountable at a later stage. This was the fact that the magnetron transmitting valve was so secret that there would be no question of flying it over enemy territory. The probability of one being recovered from a crashed RAF bomber and hence revealing its secrets to the Germans was very real.

The proposal was therefore to use a klystron instead, for this type of device was to an extent common knowledge. However, since our frustration of the summer of 1940 this type of valve was bad news. Nevertheless, a degree of optimism existed since further experimental work on klystrons had continued on the part of Oliphant and others. Accordingly, development of a suitable klystron was put in hand.

EMI had been awarded the H_2S contract and this was to include co-operation in the development and production of a klystron to take the place of the magnetron in the transmitter/receiver (T/R) unit. In the meantime the T/R unit with magnetron as developed for centimetre AI would be used for the initial trials. Very promising results were to be achieved in these early trials using the magnetron.

In spite of months of concerted effort on the part of both EMI and TRE, the results with klystrons were most disappointing. Try as they may, the combined teams could not manufacture a klystron which produced an output power to approach that of the magnetron. In short, H_2S without the magic magnetron was effectively useless.

Now followed the great debate. The TRE directorate, the RAF high command and the War Cabinet, including the Prime Minister in person with his several scientific advisers, all became embroiled in the pros and cons of flying with magnetrons or not flying with magnetrons.

In the course of searching for solutions there was a suggestion that perhaps the T/R unit could be fitted with an explosive device capable of rendering the magnetron indecipherable. A test with such an arrangement was therefore set up using an old grounded aircraft.

To everyone's consternation the powerful explosion blew a man-sized hole in the side of the fuselage whilst leaving the magnetron with its solid copper body largely intact. An expert could have copied it without difficulty.

Desperation had now set in. Bomber Command, having from the tests sampled a very useful navigational aid, were adamant that they were not prepared to forgo it. The debate hence reduced itself to a question of profit and loss from the possible use of the magnetron.

Upon the assumption that sooner or later the device would fall into the hands of the enemy, how much damage could be inflicted upon their capacity to wage war (and from this to what degree might it be shortened) by the aid of H_2S, before countermeasures could be developed by Germany?

At the climax of this debate tragedy struck the project. On 7 June 1942, Halifax V9977, while on a test flight with the prototype equipment, crashed in the Forest of Dean – all on board were killed.

We were all shocked, not just because it was disastrous for the project but because we had lost friends and colleagues at TRE, EMI, and in the RAF. Among those who had died was the EMI project leader, A.D. Blumlein. He was the country's foremost electronics engineer, being the man principally responsible for the design of the EMI 405-line television system which was adopted by the BBC in 1936 in preference to the Baird system. It was at that time far in advance of any other TV system worldwide. What hit ourselves the most however, was the death of our own colleague, the one whose experience over the Bristol Channel probably started the whole thing – Hensby.[2]

When the project finally recovered from this setback, from an establishment move, and from the customary problems in production, H_2S became operational in January 1943. This followed Winston Churchill's personal authorization to use the magnetron.

Almost immediately the high command's worst fears were realized. Within a matter of days of the first H_2S guided raid, a bomber was lost over occupied territory from which the vital equipment was able to be recovered by the Germans. From all accounts it seems that the more modest size of detonator finally chosen to protect the radar's secret did little to hinder investigation and understanding of the magnetron by the German experts.

It was all the more surprising, therefore, that the Germans seemed not to make a great deal of use of their acquired knowledge, apart from developing a 10 centimetre receiver called Naxos which, installed in their night-fighters, enabled them to home in on H_2S-equipped planes.

This did of course provide a serious hazard to our bombers which was only mitigated by adopting intermittent rather than continuous use of the H_2S sets during a sortie. For some inexplicable reasons however, the Germans never got round to reproducing any magnetrons.

Perhaps they were satisfied with their 50 centimetre systems or maybe they had found difficulty in penetrating the 20 centimetre barrier. As it was, it took them almost a year to produce the 10 centimetre Naxos listening set.

Watson-Watt, who had forecast the likelihood of the Germans salvaging a magnetron, had estimated that it would take the German scientists and technicians a mere two to three months to benefit from information derived from a find. Fortunately for the Allies his assessment proved to be grossly pessimistic. It was likely that he based his estimate on British wartime streamlined methods, whereas the Germans, as well as their lack of knowledge of centimetre techniques, were weighed down by their bureaucracy and lack of interdepartmental co-operation.

To their credit however, the Germans' overall anti-aircraft defences from late 1942 onwards were very effective. The toll taken against Bomber Command was considerable. This was mainly due to an effectively integrated system of searchlights, AA guns, and night-fighters, all under radar control. The line stretched from Denmark to northern France and was known by the British as the Kammhuber Line after the General of that name who was responsible for its creation.

Compared to the limited depth available to the RAF Fighter Command and the army's AA Command for the defence of Britain (particularly London), the occupied territory gave the Germans an area of operation some 600 miles in breadth and an average of 150 miles in depth before the border of the Reich was reached. Then, of course, once the massed raids were initiated by Air Chief Marshal Sir Arthur Harris in mid-1942 there were bombers in plenty for the Luftwaffe to hunt.

From its introduction in January 1943 H_2S went from strength to strength. In all, there were six versions from the initial Mark I crash programme on S band (9.8 centimetres), with X band (3 centimetre) variants (Marks III and IV) and even a K band (1¼ centimetres) version. From the early models with simple map presentation there were various degrees of sophistication introduced in successive models, including such features as blind-bombing facilities, and 'Fishpond', an auxilliary display unit designed to give warning of rear approaching fighters which was derived by processing the basic H_2S signal.

* * *

What of centimetre ASV in the meantime? Here was a double irony. First, when Hensby made his Bristol Channel flight which set the whole H_2S project in motion, he was after all out to test the potentialities of the 10 centimetre equipment for ASV. Secondly it was Air Chief Marshal Sir Phillip Joubert while Assistant Chief of Air Staff (Radio) at the Air Ministry who in his pep talk to TRE sowed the seed which became H_2S.

Now Joubert found himself appointed AOC in C Coastal Command just at a time when what was needed to help in the Battle of the Atlantic was centimetre ASV.

He was hence in competition with Bomber Command's AOC in C Sir Arthur Harris, but unfortunately Coastal Command was lower down in the pecking order. He therefore had to stand impotently by while the arguments raged over magnetron security and while H_2S production was held up by the abortive klystron development. Ironically none of this kerfuffle would have occurred had Coastal Command been first in the queue, for with their centimetre radar (which would be hardly distinguishable from H_2S), the precious magnetron could have been safely flown over the ocean.

Eventually Joubert's Command got its Mk III ASV early in 1943, soon after Bomber Command had the go-ahead to fly their H_2S. It was not too soon because the U- boats had been equipped with receivers warning them of the approach of Coastal Command aircraft using Mk II (1½ metre) ASV.

With the new radar came some useful new weapons such as rockets, which were to prove more effective than depth charges against the U-boats, provided they could be caught on the surface. This was often done successfully at night with the aid of the Leigh light, a powerful searchlight slung under the plane's fuselage.

The most bizarre of these new weapons, however, was the product of our radar scanner manufacturers, Nash and Thompson, at whose works I saw the mock-up. It was a large cannon, much the size of a Bofors gun, which could be wound out through a trapdoor at the rear of the aircraft. The desired angle for firing would be set by the plane going into a climb at the critical moment.

In the fullness of time the U-boats were equipped with 10 centimetre listening sets and it looked as if Mark III ASV would share the fate of Mark II. Then a bright TRE scientist named Callick came up with a clever but simple device to fool the U-boat radio operators into thinking the hunter aircraft had changed its direction.

The most valuable of the new innovations was undoubtedly the least costly, even though the team concerned included no less than five fellows of the Royal Society. This was the Operational Research Unit headed by Professor P.M.S. Blackett.

Their means were entirely cerebral and involved no costly hardware or scarce productive capacity. On the contrary, the methodology resulted in a more effective use of existing resources. Based principally on statistical analysis, the technique also involved a detailed and logical study of all the factors involved in a given operation.

Throughout the war the battle with the U-boats was a continuous and ding-dong affair. While the initiative was with the U-boats the Allies sustained enormous losses in shipping and precious lives. As new weapons and methods became available to Coastal Command and the Navy the tables would be turned for a while, only to be countered by some new development. In undersea warfare there were none so clever and indeed so cunning as the Germans.

Footnotes

1. We were not far wrong. BN stood for 'Blind Navigation', as confirmed by Lovell. R.V. Jones in his book *Most Secret War* gives it as TF, standing for 'Town Finding'. This was never the case.

2. Both Lovell and Curran were due to go on this flight but were prevented at the last moment by other commitments.

13 The Navy Comes Aboard

At the beginning of 1942 the first application of the new 3 centimetre technology had been chosen. These were to be two complementary systems for the Fleet Air Arm.

To carry out these projects a minor rearrangement of our centimetre groups was required. My own group under Skinner and Atkinson were to move on from wholly basic research to the development of an AI system for the new Fairey Firefly, which would provide a carrier-borne night-fighter for the navy. At the same time Warren's group, who were soon to complete their work on the centimetre height finder, would become responsible for an ASV system for another new naval aircraft – the Barracuda.

The transmitter/receiver units would be common to both systems, the work being shared between our two groups while each would be responsible for the development of the individual and distinctive aerial systems and display electronics.

Contractors for each of the two applications were allocated. This was the responsibility of MAP's Controller of Communications Equipment (CCE) who was Sir Robert Renwick, pre-war chairman of the London Electricity Board. They would be development contracts, the contractors co-operating with TRE in the development prior to engaging in the required large-scale production of sets.

There was a large measure of luck in these allocations which appeared to be made on the basis of Buggin's turn. Warren's group drew the lucky number for they had the services of Bush Radio, who proved to be masters of electronic layout and design.

They were ideally suited to producing compact and lightweight equipment for airborne use.

We on the other hand drew the short straw and were given BTH of Rugby, which turned out to be a disastrous choice. It was not that they weren't very capable engineers, but that for a compact airborne application they were in the wrong league. They were, after all, mainly heavy electrical engineers in the business of building power stations and as such were far more suited to designing and building equipment for the navy's ships than for the navy's not over-large aircraft. It was indeed an entirely different design technique and I, at the tender age of twenty-three, was at one stage sent up to the mighty Rugby works to show them how to set about laying out miniaturized electronics.

Both the Firefly and the Barracuda were the product of Fairey Aviation at Hayes, Middlesex. To facilitate the design of the radars which were to be squeezed into their overcrowded interiors the firm provided full-size wooden mock-ups of the main part of each fuselage. They duly arrived at Leeson House early in 1942.

The Navy for their part provided us with some professionals as advisors, and some hands to assist us in the practical work. The latter followed the practice already established with the RAF by which in exchange for the loan of personnel, their people received valuable advance training in the course of their work.

Of the professionals two were civilian scientists – Derek Smith, a young PhD. (whose brother Graham was to become Astronomer Royal) allotted to Warren's group and a jolly Irishman, Jack Dalby, who came to us.

The uniformed staff were commanded by Lt. Le Fevre (called 'Lefty' by his men) with the support of two second lieutenants ('subbies'). The hands were a number of electrical artificers (known as 'killicks' in the trade) – they were radio technicians equivalent to the RAF radar mechanics – and to keep them in order there was a tall, experienced petty officer. The PO's attention was, however, somewhat distracted by the presence of two very smart Wren petty officers (all Wrens appeared attractively smart), one of whom he courted and married before the war had ended. Her companion also came to be courted and married by one of our scientists. This surprised us all because he was a quiet, introverted fellow whose whole life appeared to be devoted to the design of electronic circuits – or so we thought!

The day this motley crew arrived, the hands marched smartly into the lab carrying kit-bags and tool boxes. We were made well aware that the navy had come aboard when their front man called out: 'Where do we stow our kit, on the deck?' They soon made themselves at home and with all the naval terminology it began to feel as if the lab was afloat.

They all acted as though they were storm-proven sailors. In fact, Swanage was the nearest they had been to the sea since joining up. We imagined that they were putting on an act to impress us landlubbers.

I was to learn differently when months later I went to a meeting with Lt. Le Fevre at HMS *Aeriel* near Warrington. Here at an establishment firmly placed upon good Lancashire soil, the nearest water being the Manchester Ship Canal, the ambience was totally nautical. When a ruddy-faced old boy in gold-braided RNR uniform was heard asking to be directed to the 'Captain's cabin' I thought the joke had gone far enough.

During the homeward journey I expressed my amusement at these land-locked nautics to Lefty who promptly put me right. He explained that this was a deliberate policy, justified particularly in wartime with its general call-up. By acting on shore establishments as if they were ships, raw recruits, when finally getting to sea (which could prove a traumatic experience), would, to a degree at least, find a familiar environment.

The Navy lads were soon well integrated into our world of experimentation and provided valuable effort. Meanwhile the professionals were able to offer guidance relating to operational aspects where they differed from those of the RAF.

The Barracuda system was relatively simple in conception, being in essence a compact kind of H_2S. Our Firefly radar on the other hand was to be the most complex and advanced of the day. It was to be the first application of F.C. Williams's innovative lock-follow system for which the 3 centimetre radar was admirably suited.

As the Firefly, a two-seater aircraft, had a single engine, the scanner was to be accommodated in a perspex nacelle placed mid-way along one wing with a dummy nacelle on the other to balance it.

The electronics based on the F.C. Williams prototype were quite sophisticated and demanded the skill of a good circuit-designer for their development. This was placed in the capable hands of Arthur Cockroft, a young JSO.

The heart of the system was a feature called an 'auto-strobe'. This was a time-measuring pulse which could be set to lock-on to a received radar pulse from a selected target and thence to track it, just as a theatre spotlight follows a performer on stage. By analysing the movement of the auto-strobe in the time domain all the required data could be derived with which to direct and lock the scanner on to target.

The same electrical information would be used in composing the display. The principal display unit and the controls were for use by the observer while a spot display showing the direction of the target from the aircraft (akin to a gunsight) was provided for the pilot. Initially this latter display was a miniature cathode-ray tube viewed direct, but subsequently a version was developed which projected the display on to the pilot's windscreen – this was one of the earliest applications of this technique.

An additional feature was a meter which displayed the speed difference (positive or negative) between the attacking aircraft and the hunted. Its scale measured up to the order of 600 mph (actually shown as knots for the navy) to cater for the likelihood of a head-on approach.

Like the ill-fated Nimrod system, which the Firefly AI radar pre-dated by about forty years, the project became a victim of its own complexity. It set out to accomplish much but failed to meet expectations.

Development had reached its zenith, and at BTH

provisioning and tooling-up were at an advanced stage (production in excess of a hundred sets had been planned, which was quite ambitious for equipment of this type), when the death knell began to sound.

The RAF had a Fighter Interception Unit (FIU) which among its various duties was responsible for flight-testing and approving AI radars prior to their being introduced into service. The 10 centimetre AI Mark VIII had been so tested by the legendary 'Catseye' Cunningham who had given it his enthusiastic approval. It was logical therefore that the Admiralty should avail themselves of FIU's expertise to evaluate the Firefly system on their behalf, since AI radars were a new departure for the Fleet Air Arm.

It was to our misfortune (but possibly to the Navy's ultimate deliverance) that the person to carry out the evaluation was Wing Commander Derek Jackson.

Here was a remarkable person, a man of many parts. Before the war he had been a wealthy man about town – a socialite. He was an accomplished horseman and in addition to hunting had also rode in the Grand National on a number of occasions. He was married to Pamela, one of the famed Mitford sisters, which made him brother-in-law to Sir Oswald Mosley (who had been interned for the duration) and to Unity Mitford who had earned a degree of notoriety in the thirties by her admiration for, and acquaintance with, Adolf Hitler and other prominent members of the Nazi Party.

He was, however, no playboy (nor indeed a fascist sympathizer) but surprisingly a well-qualified scientist of repute, having been one of Professor Lindemann's team at Oxford's Clarendon Laboratory. Characteristically, he had chosen active service in the RAF rather than becoming a boffin like his erstwhile Clarendon colleagues. His scientific talents were soon recognized by the RAF in which service he was to rise to become Wing Commander and Chief Airborne Radar Officer in Fighter Command, and to be awarded the DFC.

All this made him a formidable examiner of the Firefly radar. His judgement would prove final, for in addition to his undeniable scientific qualifications and airborne radar experience, the fact that he was on first-name terms with many top people including Professor Lindemann (now Lord Cherwell) gave him considerable clout.

He made a series of test flights in the prototype Firefly together with a companion aircraft which took the part of an enemy. He was very critical of many of the system's features, but the lock-follow system in his view had certain fundamental limitations. In spite of the fact that by then the equipment had begun to roll off the production line, at his recommendation the project was axed.

This was a body blow to our group and so it was hardly surprising that the name of Derek Jackson hit rock bottom. Some said that they doubted whether this 'self-opinionated fellow' had ever approved anything that was not of his own making. Others were convinced that it was 'Clarendon bias', since centimetre radar had been the creation of Cavendish men.

All this was, of course, sour grapes on our part brought on by the realization that more than two years had been wasted. Our innermost selves, however, knew that Jackson's objections to a lock-follow system were valid. Apart from the fact that while the scanner was locked on to a target, no other aircraft that might be in the vicinity could be observed on the radar (which in a combat situation was obviously undesirable), there was one fatal flaw which killed the project stone dead.

It was discovered in the flight trials that should the hunted aircraft, on to which the radar had locked, suddenly take a rapid dive, the scanner would be unable to follow in time and would hence drop out of lock. Although the system would immediately revert to a search mode, the target aircraft would inevitably have been lost.

To fill the breach the Navy opted for an American 3 centimetre radar called ASH. As a piece of production engineering it was indeed a thing of beauty. With the exception of the remote display for the observer, which was very little larger than the six-inch diameter cathode-ray tube itself, the whole of the radar was packaged in a torpedo-shaped container about five feet long and a foot in diameter which was slung under the plane's fuselage. The sharp end of the torpedo was a perspex nose-cone covering the miniature scanner. The scanning was relatively simple, giving a range/azimuth display.

It was designed and manufactured to perfection by Western Electric, and for anyone like myself concerned with layout and production engineering design it was worthy of serious and detailed study. By comparison our own set of equipment was as a DC3 to a Concorde.

Our set had got completely out of hand. In the first place we were stuck with the overweight and bulky BTH packaging, even though the internal layouts had been improved. Then, as development proceeded, the outfit began to sprout a whole array of add-on units as either the Navy had asked for extra facilities or our own team had had bursts of inspiration.

As the installation grew, so its weight increased until finally to the chagrin of Fairey's design engineers we had succeeded in displacing the plane's centre of gravity by all of three inches; a not insignificant amount, the aeronautical men took pains to inform us.

To restore the balance it was necessary for them to stretch the fuselage to enable the engine to be moved forward. The principal culprit in putting on weight was the least suspected – the interconnecting cables. When all these screened connector assemblies were coiled up and gathered together the total weight was unbelievable.

Ironically, for all the brilliance of the American radar's design, its performance, particularly in terms of the detection range, was no match for our own system.

It seemed that there was nothing but the scrap heap for the product of our hard work, when early in June 1944 Londoners awoke to a new and unnerving sound. The first of Hitler's threatened secret weapons had arrived – the V1 or buzz bomb, as it became known.

These pilotless ram-jet aircraft, which were in fact flying bombs, were small and fast. This made them difficult to intercept and destroy. For several weeks the enemy had it all their own way, although more failed on launch or got lost on the way than were shot down. Then, in the light of experience, an integrated plan for defence was put into effect. The AA batteries which had hitherto been stationed in a ring around London were moved to the Kent coast where they could operate more successfully, whilst at the same time giving Fighter Command free rein over the approach area to the capital. These new arrangements, plus the fact that the latest fighters – the Typhoons – were used, began to turn the tide in Britain's favour.

The unique nature of the V1 posed a whole new set of problems in defence. In this connection it was considered that our lock-follow radar would be ideally suited to increasing the speed and precision of AA gun-laying.

A crash programme was therefore initiated to adapt a quantity of the otherwise unwanted sets. The scanner was fitted with a larger diameter mirror and given a suitable mounting. The electronics were modified to enable the electrical data representing the directional co-ordinates, range, and target speed, to be fed directly into the gun's predictor, so dispensing with the slower human element in the gun's control chain.

Everyone concerned worked round the clock, which resulted in sets becoming operational within three weeks. Once again, however, the 3 centimetre lock-follow system was to be stillborn, for the Allied Expeditionary Force had since D Day fought its way up the Normany coast, overrunning the V1 launch sites in the process. It was an ignominious end to an ambitious project. The group, facing disbandment, said farewell to their naval companions who presumably departed to learn all about ASH; maybe even to find themselves at sea!

Our efforts were not entirely wasted, for out of the debris of the Firefly project came a set of basic 3 centimetre units, namely: the transmitter/receiver, modulator, power unit, and a range of waveguide fittings all of which provided the core components of many other systems. The most notable of these were the 3 centimetre versions of H_2S which, because the shorter wavelength made possible a narrower beam aerial than with 10 centimetres, enhanced resolution and hence became useful. As for the lock-follow technology, this was merely ahead of its time. It was to come into its own much later with the age of guided weapons.

14 'We're off to Prangmere'

At lunch at Durnford early in 1942 we were joined at our table by Derrick Garrard. As Dr Lewis's PA he had been among those who had welcomed and briefed us new boys on our very first day at Worth Matravers. Now he was based in London on loan to Dr R.V. Jones's scientific intelligence team.

'What's the latest then?' enquired one of our number who was aware that Derrick was frequently concerned with 'interesting projects.' 'We have a very interesting photograph – a large dish,' he replied with an enigmatic smile. He was saying no more and we knew better than to pump him.

A few weeks later, on the night of 27 March, a commando force raided a German radar station perched high on the coast of Normandy at a little place called Bruneval. It was of the latest type, code-named by the Germans as 'Würzburg' – it had a large dish!

The object of the raid was to gain as much knowledge as possible of this radar, at least by inspection but ideally by the capture of the principal items of equipment. It was a combined operation with paratroopers taking the station, and a naval force providing back-up and receiving what equipment could be removed.

It was of course essential that someone with an intimate knowledge of radar equipment should take part, but the powers that be ruled that this must not be a TRE scientist. A brave RAF flight sergeant by the name of Cox volunteered for this dangerous operation and after suitable commando training and detailed briefing on what was required technically he made the drop with the paratroopers.

A TRE scientific officer did accompany the naval force; he was D.H. Priest, one of the original Bawdsey team. Had the commando force secured complete and uninterrupted occupation of the enemy site he would have been allowed to land. This was not to be, as there was a measure of resistance by German forces which involved some shooting. Nevertheless the flight sergeant carried out his appointed task most efficiently, returning not only with much valuable information but with all the vital units. Priest, although denied the excitement of landing and inspecting the station for himself, was on his return to TRE at least able to bask in reflected glory as the custodian of the equipment which it was then his task to investigate.

Such operations inevitably invite reprisals. The government was therefore concerned that TRE at its south-coastal location was particularly vulnerable should the Germans contemplate a return match. In consequence the establishment was put on a state of alert at the next period of full moon. I had married the previous summer and we were now living in a small flat less than a hundred yards from the seashore. Although it was nearly April the nights were clear, bright, and cold which made us feel particularly exposed, and for several nights we went to bed quite expecting to be awakened by the sound of gunfire.

Although we might have been somewhat apprehensive at the thought of waking to a heavy German hand beating on our front door in the middle of the night, this was nothing compared to the anxiety of the night-duty RAF radar operators at D site, Worth Matravers. This was a 1½ metre experimental CHL installation perched on a rocky shelf hacked out of the cliff top at St Alban's Head. Following an advance warning the key items of equipment had to be loaded into their light Hillman van as instructed. The van then had to be reversed (in the dark) to the cliff edge where, should the enemy arrive on the scene, the handbrake would be released and the vehicle pushed over the edge to disappear below the angry breakers at the foot of the rocky cliffs, a sheer 200 feet below. It would have been with a considerable degree of trepidation that the driver backed his vehicle to the very edge of destruction, trusting his colleagues to give him the timely signal when to stop.

The period of full moon duly passed and we all settled back to concentrating on the work in hand. Then rumours began to proliferate that a move was in the offing, but the outlandish destination bandied about lent no credence to the wild speculations. This had gone on for about a couple of weeks, when one morning we were called to assemble in the lecture hall where the superintendent was to address us.

Rowe was on top form that morning and his talk was lively and amusing. Doubtless his intention was to soften the impact that a total move of both home and workplace would make on his staff – for some this would be the third time in less than as many years. He began by explaining that the Prime Minister personally had ordered that TRE be moved before the next full moon. But where to? That was what we were all anxious to learn. Before answering that question however, he was to keep us on tenterhooks while he entertained us with an account of his travels throughout the preceding week.

It had been a bizarre 'house-hunting' adventure with 'men from the ministry' in the role of estate agents. He had been accompanied by Sidney Jefferson, one of his division heads of long standing from Bawdsey days – doubtless a wise choice since not only would he have been a good judge of what scientific groups would need, but he had already had experience of the two previous moves of the establishment.

It soon transpired that the Ministry of Works, whose job it was among other things to provide office space for government departments, had strange ideas as to what was suitable for research scientists. With reluctance bordering on alarm, Rowe was taken into the bowels of the earth to view a disused underground factory. One look and he was not surprised it was disused! Back in the daylight he was searching his mind for adequate words of condemnation when an 'officer of the realm' as he described the man from Whitehall, stepped into a muddy puddle up to his knees. The decision was made – TRE would not be coming here.

The first of the places that warranted serious consideration was Marlborough School. It was, however, somewhat remote from any industrial centres, and since the town drainage system was hardly adequate for the existing inhabitants a large influx of people would most likely prove catastrophic. Then, following a suggestion of Dr B.V. Bowden, one of TRE's senior staff, the survey party took a look at Malvern College and were immediately relieved to find that it fulfilled most of the requirements. Between the college and the town it appeared that there would be sufficient working and living accommodation, and above all the fact that the college was on sloping ground overlooking the Vale of Evesham made it as ideal as any inland site for the radar work. Moreover, Birmingham and other industrial cities were close by.

And so it was that Rowe came to announce that we would all be moving to Malvern – lock, stock and barrel – and in the shortest time, commencing immediately. It would be a mammoth task; the establishment was by then some 800 strong, and with families the total number of persons to be moved with their effects was possibly double that figure. But the greatest part of the undertaking was the transportation of every item of equipment, which ranged from mere handfuls of electronic components to man-sized transmitter cubicles, workshop machinery, and a number of seventy-foot lattice aerial masts.

The removal of this vast amount of varied equipment was, we were told, to be put in the hands of the emergency removal organization which had been set up by the government following the experience of the aftermath of the blitz on Coventry. This was in effect Pickford's Removals nationalized and was organized to have the capacity of removing the furniture and effects of a whole town.

Top priority was being given by central government to whatever services and material help would be needed to effect the rapid relocation of the establishment, its staff, and their families. In this connection a billeting order was being placed on the town as a necessary measure to provide initial quarters for the overwhelming numbers about to descend upon the town.

Finally, and with a noticeable twinkle in his eye, Rowe told us that Malvern appeared to be a town that didn't know there was a war on – young people could be seen going to dances in evening dress as before the war. It was hence up to us to show them what it was all about! With consummate skill he had engendered a feeling of excitement and anticipation to the extent that we instinctively cheered. We were ready for action.

And so began a most dramatic three weeks which was the remarkably short time it took to transport this major technical establishment with its strange and complex equipment away inland to the very heart of the country. It was to make a travelling circus look like a mere Sunday afternoon picnic. In retrospect it was one of the most significant events of our lives. It was hard, traumatic, and left many lingering problems, but none would say that it lacked exhilaration.

*   *   *

Without further delay, preparations for the move were underway. An advance party of representatives was assembled from each of TRE's divisions and despatched to Malvern. Their principal task was to oversee the work being carried out within the college campus by a vast army of tradesmen drafted from all around the Midlands. There were builders, carpenters, electricians, telephone engineers and general labourers, in all numbering several hundreds. Their job was to convert this stately residential seminary into an advanced scientific establishment in double quick time. Classrooms would become engineering workshops, housemasters' quarters offices, and the dormitories, which had enjoyed the relative luxury of being subdivided into individual cubicles (we nicknamed them 'horse boxes') had their partitions torn out and in their place lab benches were erected, together with electrical power sockets in profusion and above the benches light fittings by the yard.

Concurrently with all this industrial activity, another party of TRE volunteers were assisting Malvern's Town Clerk, who had been appointed Billeting Officer under the Defence Regulations with the task of visiting each and every home in all six parts of greater Malvern to assess what accommodation would be available. This was a monumental task which would have completely overwhelmed the wartime depleted ranks of the Town Hall staff. No election canvass was ever as thorough.

The government's emergency billeting order had effectively thrown a ring around the Malverns and their environs. Any householder with a spare bedroom was obliged to take in as many as there were beds. They were not obliged to offer food, but those who were willing were listed as full billets; otherwise they were declared 'shelter billets'. Many of these were as stark as the term implied.

To give the order full effect the legislation had enclosed Malvern within an iron curtain in as much that anyone who was not directly related to a householder or who was not on essential business could not come into the town to stay. These somewhat Draconian measures made under the Defence regulations were nonetheless necessary with the imminent arrival of upwards of 1,500 persons.

Vacant premises were requisitioned to be dealt with later. There were a considerable number of large houses with vacant possession in the town and these were to be converted into flats once the initial task of accommodating everyone in temporary billets had been accomplished. Similarly, hostel accommodation for single staff would be provided in part by allocating one of the college houses (House 9), and elsewhere round the town by taking over guest houses and small hotels which were doubtless glad to see full houses again.

Responsible for the direction and administration of all these arrangements was the taxed and frequently overworked A.B. Jones. He was to be faced with overseeing no less than five such moves during his working life, but none so monumental as this rapid transplantation of TRE to Malvern.

* * *

Meanwhile, what of Malvern College itself? The news of the requisitioning came as a bombshell to its headmaster Mr H.C.A. Gaunt. It was 25 April and the start of summer term was but a week away. The first task therefore was to send a telegram of postponement to each of the 350 or so boys. Then came the seemingly hopeless undertaking to find alternative accommodation. The school was on its own; in crude terms, summarily evicted – put out on to the street without a by-your-leave, as it were. And almost straight away the first consignments began to arrive from Swanage, and the first contingent of workers descended on the place to start tearing it apart. The Ministry of Works was about as helpful as they had been to TRE. All they could offer was Berkeley Castle which effectively had no water, and an army camp near Hereford, but that was only half-built.

What made the whole affair particularly aggravating was that this had all happened before. Within days of the outbreak of the war the school had been requisitioned to make way for the Admiralty from Whitehall. Since the holocaust never came to London that autumn of 1939, the college went unoccupied. Nevertheless, Malvern boys spent a complete school year in a hastily rearranged Blenheim Palace.

Now in 1942 it seemed the school would have to disperse by houses. Then Gaunt became aware that Harrow was at that time somewhat below full strength. And so, thanks to the generosity of spirit of Mr A.P. Boissier, Harrow's acting headmaster, Malvern was able to move in with them but without losing its separate identity.

* * *

For the bulk of us back in Dorset it was an immediate start on dismantling equipment and getting it packed ready for transhipment. For this purpose a multitude of packing cases descended upon us seemingly from out of the blue. These ranged in size from the likes of the humble tea-chest to aero-engine crates of such a size that if inverted would have made capacious garden sheds. With the latter we were to learn what a mistake it was to fill them completely.

We had started the packing when one morning a man from the removal organization arrived unannounced to walk through stables rapidly looking from side to side like someone who had lost his wallet. Finally, reaching the door, he muttered the word 'six' to himself before scribbling something down on a notepad. Six of what, we wondered. Crates? Days of work? Men to shift it all?

It turned out to be six whole removal vans that were needed to transport our group's equipment alone. At the peak of the move there would be on one particular day no less than ninety removal vans on the road at the same time. The total number of van journeys for the whole move was never made known to us, but the regiment of pantechnicons was travelling back and forth for over a fortnight. To supplement this were the various vehicles of TRE's own transport section whose job it was to move the countless GL trailers used by many of TRE's groups, diesel-electric sets, and the transportable seventy-foot lattice aerial masts which had to be broken down into sections for removal on flat trailers.

Swanage was buzzing with rumour almost before the move was officially announced, but we all made an effort not to spread any details of it among those who had no business to know. Two of our naval section, Heap and Thomas, with a young RAF pilot officer belonging to the H_2S squad, were plagued in their civilian lodgings with an inquisitive landlady. They were asked point-blank where they were being moved to and knowing that the bold statement 'Secret' was not likely to satisfy her curiosity, they brightly replied 'Prangmere'.

Not being a reader of *Punch*, the dear lady was not to know that Prangmere was fictitious. It was indeed an imaginary (but not untypical) RAF air base whose CO was Squadron Leader Duff Gen ('duff gen' was RAF vernacular for false information), as regularly reported in the columns of that time-honoured satirical journal. The name was derived from the word 'prang,' meaning a crash, and the name of the veteran south-coast RAF station, Tangmere.

The landlady believed it and was satisfied, which so amused our lads that they reported it to us with glee. Little did they know that they had unwittingly conjured up a genie.

We were all busily engaged in the rather unglamorous job of dismantling equipment and getting it packed into the crates. Such occasions simply cry out for some comic relief. It soon manifested itself.

As the lids were hammered down on the crates the particular destination was painted on. Conveniently for this purpose we had as a stock-in-trade small tins of cellulose enamel in various colours which were used for marking things as well as painting pieces of equipment. Ours was Group 8 and by coincidence we were to occupy House 8 at the college, hence the crates were duly marked with the symbols 'G8 – H8'. It chanced that there was a surfeit of red tins which seemed ideal since our markings would show up boldly. But red can be a mischievous colour!

It all started with one fellow adding the innocent words 'Prangmere College' to the G8 – H8 location, but it was not long before crates were being adorned with such slogans as 'With Care – Live Prangs' – all of course in bright pillar-box red which had established itself as the hallmark of the Prangmere movement. Very soon Prangmere fever had gripped everyone apart from our seniors who were closeted in the office, doubtless anguishing over the plans of House 8 at Malvern. We had run out of slogans to paint on packing cases (and indeed run out of packing cases), so we then set about painting the place red – literally.

The whole jamboree came to an abrupt end when Dr Skinner arrived in the lab with an important visitor. They had come to see a particular piece of 3 centimetre equipment before it was crated up. The line of lights above the long bench had all been decorated with the circular logo of London Transport, and an associated sign bore the legend 'Follow the red lights to Prangmere Circus.' They were both plainly embarrassed.

Although we were all partners in the merry caper it was the unfortunate Heap and Thomas who took the rap. For their presumed sins they were smartly packed off to Malvern with the first convoy of removal vans. Just as they were about to depart they were duly warned by Jimmy Atkinson that if there was 'any red paint nonsense' when they got to Malvern they would both be off to sea! Nevertheless, a few days later we received a greetings telegram bearing the message: 'Greetings from Prangmere.' Later, when we had all arrived in Malvern, it was duly framed – in red!

* * *

After about two weeks of hard labour dismantling and packing equipment numerous van loads had been despatched to Malvern for the overworked Heap and Thomas to unpack and stack up in any odd spot not occupied by carpenters or electricians and where the floorboards had not been ripped up. All the heavy equipment and the giant aero-engine crates now (unwisely) full of material had been left until last. This would ensure that by the time the heaviest items reached Malvern, the majority of the team would also have arrived, and would be on hand for their unloading.

It was just our luck that on the last day of loading the big stuff it came on to rain, steady rain which, hour upon hour, impregnated us all with its wetness. As we manhandled the heavy loads with nothing more than lengths of pipe and battens of wood as our mechanical handling equipment, the ground, made muddy and slippery, became resistant to our attempts to impart forward motion. We knew what it must have been like for the builders of Stonehenge. On the other hand, they were more fortunate than us – there were many more of them and they had a lot more time!

We all finished like drowned rats. It was the end – end of the week, end of our time in the stables, end of our collective tether – a Friday never to be forgotten.

15 Exodus

Even for Swanage, a holiday resort, it must have been an impressive number of coaches which left the town that morning. It was a motley cavalcade of vehicles old and new, supplied by operators large and small from around Dorset and Hampshire.

It was a perfect day to enjoy the rolling English countryside in its lush green shroud of late spring. The procession was heading due north, and we were soon admiring the broad sweep of the Wiltshire Downs. Spread out ahead were more of our coaches whilst following behind at respectable intervals were yet more. Frequently we would overtake one of the small convoys of large navy-blue Pickford's removal vans.

Apart from military traffic (of which there was little on this Sunday in May) the roads across country were relatively quiet throughout the war. This was as well on this occasion, for contributing to TRE's virtual monopoly of the route were those members of staff driving their own cars, each with a complement of passengers. Surely no single organization save an army had ever moved such a volume of men and material as did TRE that memorable weekend.

How and when our bicycles reached Malvern I cannot remember, but at least one fellow managed to transport his in novel fashion. He was one of the Naval Section stationed at Hurn airfield where they had a selection of naval aircraft including a number of Swordfish, those remarkable old lumbering biplanes affectionately called 'Stringbags'. All the aircraft at Hurn were having to be flown up to the new airfield near Malvern; hence it was that a Swordfish took off with a bicycle lashed to one side.

Following a lunch-time stop, it was mid-afternoon when, as our coach descended the long hill down to Cheltenham, we had our first view of the Malvern Hills. Little more than a half-hour later our coach pulled up outside the gaunt Gothic facade of the Main Building of Malvern College.

Set up in the stone-flagged foyer were the reception staff to whom we reported, receiving in return the addresses of our respective billets. A large street plan of all the Malverns shown ranged around the line of hills was on display to help us find our billets.

My wife and I were relatively lucky, having been allotted a billet just a mile to the east of the college. Before searching it out, however, we had been advised to visit the canteen to take an evening meal.

In the fullness of time a purpose-built canteen would be erected within the college grounds, but until that happy day we would all be taking three meals a day including weekends in the Winter Gardens.

To feed the best part of a thousand individuals three full meals a day, the elegant concert-hall-cum-ballroom of the Winter Gardens had been requisitioned. The spacious interior was filled to capacity with army type barrack tables and forms. Kitchens were set up in the area beyond the stage, staffed in the first instance by WAAF's who, understandably, did not take kindly to feeding civilians. Additional help was provided by Malvern's WVS. All this must have been the talk of the town for many incredulous locals would come and peer at us through the glass doors. We felt like animals in a zoo.

By the end of the first week a civilian staff had been recruited together with the first of what was to be a long line of canteen managers. These in wartime appeared to be of a doubtful genre, for their failures ranged from plain incompetence and lack of genuine catering experience to downright dishonesty. The prime case of the latter was the fellow who finished up in jail through selling off our best meat on the black market. We had at that time been making jokes about eating horse meat – we probably were!

And so that first evening, having had our canteen meal, we set off in search of our billet. Leaving the Winter Gardens we climbed the hilly main street called Church Street and at the top where it joined the Worcester Road we paused to look around. The top of town was crowded with local families out in their Sunday best. They stood and watched in amazement as a convoy of our trailers attempted to negotiate the turning at the top of the steep hill. They must have wondered what it was all about, particularly when Dr Warren's giant CMH dish mounted on a four-wheel flat trailer arrived on the scene. These strange devices were hitherto unseen in this neck of the woods.

We found our shelter billet without difficulty along a quiet, secluded road not far from the town centre. It was a picturesque cottage in a delightful country-style garden nicely shaded beneath mature trees. Its name was 'Ronkswood' and its owner was a dear old gentleman well into his nineties. The only other member of the household was his housekeeper, who welcomed us and showed us up to our room.

That first morning at 'Ronkswood' we rose in good time and were soon on our way to the Winter Gardens, looking forward to breakfast. We were somewhat taken aback upon our arrival to find that a long queue had already formed outside the building, which soon multiplied behind us. Even the spacious hall could accommodate only a proportion of our total number at any one time.

The queue each lunch time was even longer, but we all accepted these trials with but a modicum of complaint tempered with a large measure of good humour. At least these hardships were shared among all ranks from storemen to superintendents.

The first week in Malvern for TRE as an institution was far from propitious. The rain of our last working day in Dorset had caught up with us in the Midlands and lodged against the hills like seaweed caught on rocks, showing little inclination to move on. It just rained down upon us hour after hour, day after day, invading the stoutest of raincoats.

It was hence ironic that our first task upon arrival at Malvern College was to unload and manhandle into our allotted college building the heavy equipment we had so painfully laboured with on that last wet day at Leeson House.

Several squads of able seamen from HMS *Duke*, the nearby naval training establishment, were drafted in to help us during the first few days, and we were most grateful for their help. At least the rain never bothered them, equipped as they were with their oilskins. They even brought a mobile crane with them which naturally was in very great demand around the campus. We waited our turn for it to lift the heaviest of our loads, but when it finally arrived there was insufficient space outside our building for it to operate to any advantage. We were back to our stone-age rollers and wooden battens.

After a morning of such toil we would trudge wearily like drowned rats to the Winter Gardens to queue in our sodden clothing for lunch. The same sorry process was repeated for the evening meal. Morale was beginning to sag. Then on the second day in the queue a message filtered down the line that there was a good film showing at the Festival Theatre; it was called *Hellzapoppin* and featured a pair of unknown comedians called Olsen and Johnson. It was uproariously funny throughout for it featured every gag, comic stunt, and item of trick photography ever seen before. Hence each evening the Festival Theatre was filled to capacity – by TRE staff. It proved a heaven-sent tonic for one and all.

At the end of the war, TRE's own concert party put on a show at the Winter Gardens for the benefit of the town. The chairman of Malvern Council was guest of honour. It was their all-time best show and played to a full house. At the end of the performance Rowe made a short speech, thanking the people of Malvern for accommodating and even tolerating his establishment for the past three years. He emphasized how worried he was, that first terrible week of our arrival, fearing that the establishment might not survive – such an eventuality would have had a grave effect on the conduct of the war. One thing saved TRE, he stated in all seriousness – the film *Hellzapoppin*!

There were others like TRE who made the move on a parallel course, undoubtedly suffering the same trials and tribulations.

They were our opposite numbers of the War Department –
Cockcroft's staff at ADRDE. They were moved from a quite
desirable and roomy spot near the coast at Christchurch to
occupy a somewhat uninspiring corner of Malvern part-way up
the hill at North Malvern at a place called Pale Manor.

And so it was that these two major establishments were
moved complete with all their equipment, staff and families
some 150 miles – all within the space of three weeks.

* * *

June brought a welcome change in the weather – the sun came
out. Now we could appreciate the surroundings and revise our
opinions of the place to which reluctantly we had all been
brought. Our initial reaction to the town was aptly if irreverently
epitomized by one of the lads as: 'The only graveyard in the
country having street lighting and its own bus service.' Now,
heartened by the appearance of the early summer sun, we
realized how mistaken and unfair had been our prejudgement.
Beneath clear skies we could now see and appreciate the
grandeur of the Malvern Hills so beloved by Elgar.

The college grounds were delightful even when encumbered
with all the impediments of a wartime scientific establishment.
The campus was more like a densely wooded estate than the
conventional parade ground style quadrangle. From the
commanding height of the majestic Gothic Main Building –
usually the headmaster's domain but now that of our Chief
Superintendent, A.P. Rowe – the ground sloped steadily
downward to its furthest boundary: the railway embankment of
what was then the Great Western Railway.

The central feature of these verdant grounds was the Senior
Turf, a broad green terrace mid-way down the sloping terrain.
Generations of groundsmen had lovingly nurtured this precious
sward; it was hence understandable that the headmaster was
most anxious that no harm should befall their priceless turf.

Rowe was adamant that the Senior Turf should remain
inviolate. At the briefing before the move he made it clear that if

he saw anyone as much as walking across the turf they would be disciplined. No one ever did.

The lower terraced area was the Junior Turf, but unlike its senior counterpart it was replaceable, as any suburban lawn might be. Here during the ensuing months would be built the main stores and the canteen. Upon completion of the latter, the Winter Gardens would be returned to the citizens of Malvern.

The college houses, of which there were ten, including School House, mostly became laboratories and offices for the duration and were variously situated around the periphery, each in its own enclosure. There was a library, museum, sports pavilion, gymnasium, squash courts, and a chapel. All but the latter were pressed into service.

Work on the large and bulky aerial systems involving the latticed towers and other large structures was carried out on the college sports field. This was several hundred yards away beyond the railway embankment, and was on flat ground. The end nearest St Andrew's Road was given over to the Transport Department, for whom buildings were erected, whilst alongside there was plenty of space for parking the large number and wide variety of vehicles TRE now possessed.

Some semblance of order had been attempted in labs and offices, but only to a limited extent on account of the pervasive presence of the rag-tag army of builders and electricians. It was not just the upheaval of the building operations which was bothering us, but the general conduct of the workers themselves.

They were a tough bunch and entirely without conscience. Desirable stores and particularly hand tools were disappearing. So blatant was this illicit traffic that officially issued hand tools, easily recognizable, could be seen in contractors' own tool boxes with no attempt having been made at concealment. Any attempt to retrieve them was ill advised however, since such action could predictably invite a punch-up.

Rowe was extremely worried about the situation, not only with regard to the obvious amount of theft, but because of the risk to security. Hence, having asked for our forbearance in accepting a reduced rate of working on the alterations, he gave the whole motley crew its marching orders. In their place was recruited a smaller, better managed workforce from the locality with which conditions rapidly improved.

As for our own group, reinstating the experimental centimetre sets had its problems. No longer could they remain in their trailers. Instead the equipment had to be removed and installed in the upper floor rooms of House 8 where a clear view across the countryside could be had.

What was to bug us, however, was the fact that we were without the Isle of Wight which had played such an important part in working up the efficiency of our centimetre sets. It had provided an ideal target, returning a well-defined series of echoes at a useful distance. This was because the sea between us produced comparatively small radar responses, leaving a clear, uncluttered display.

Admittedly we now had an island of sorts. This was Bredon Hill some twelve miles away, across the Vale of Evesham. This 'island,' however, was surrounded by a 'sea' of green fields with hedgerows and trees. Dotted about were numerous buildings, telegraph poles and electrical pylons, all of which produced a whole gamut of echoes. No longer were we able to show visitors clear, convincing radar pictures, and furthermore no longer in the pioneering atmosphere of a crowded interior of a trailer out in a field. Even the most successful of demonstrations would not have the same impact on VIPs when given in a bright warm room of House 8. And so the trailers which had served us well for the best part of two years were to be consigned ignominiously to the transport field. We were not to know then that they would all be needed again before the war ended.

*   *   *

Although the prime purpose of the move was to deny the enemy the opportunity to stage a Bruneval type raid on TRE, advantage was being taken to effect a general expansion. Hence our original centimetre group under the joint leadership of Dee and

Skinner was to be split in two physically, whereas in the previous six months we had been separated by the invisible wall of secrecy by the H_2S project. Now each half would become a division in its own right, each embracing a number of groups.

Dee's people including Dr Lovell, now wholly responsible for H_2S, were installed in the Preston lab. This was the college's newly built science laboratory situated a little further down the hill from House 8. It was a beautifully appointed building and being purpose-made for science it required little alteration. Being lower down the hill, however, it did not have a clear outlook for testing radar systems. This disadvantage was overcome by erecting a wooden hut on the roof which conveniently happened to be flat.

Skinner's division was to include Dr Warren's group and our own under Jimmy Atkinson. Both groups would continue to be involved with the 3 centimetre systems for the Fleet Air Arm. Also to be included were basic research groups concerned with the further development of waveguide techniques and aerial systems; under the leadership of yet another Cambridge scientist – Dr S. Devons – work on an even shorter wavelength, namely 1¼ centimetres, was initiated. Skinner's wild conjecture of the summer of 1940 was fast becoming fact.

In House 8 Jimmy and Skinner shared the capacious house-master's study for an office. It was a lofty ground-floor room adjacent to the well-proportioned Victorian front entrance to the building. Bookcases lined the walls, and since they had few books needing the shelves these became a convenient repository for all manner of sundry items of equipment.

Some of these items were potentially interesting exhibits intended to impress influential visitors, but there were also samples that certain of these same visitors had brought for us to test and evaluate. Frequently a handy roll of drawing prints diplomatically laid over a particular item would save the embarrassment of a visitor seeing dust collecting on his brainchild. This was not exactly indolence on our part, although a premium on available effort to test such items did vie with a lack of faith in the viability of the more way-out devices.

* * *

After the first two weeks in our shelter billet we were fortunate to find a vacancy in a full billet. No longer would we need to queue at the Winter Gardens for our breakfast and evening meal. We were made most welcome in the home of a jolly, if a little off-beat, family with whom we were to live comfortably for the best part of a year. We moved on when we were allocated a pair of furnished rooms where we could cater for ourselves. Soon after, we heard that they had gone to spend a holiday in Bournemouth, having learnt (doubtless from ourselves) how delightful and relatively unmolested by the Luftwaffe was this seaside town. They never came back.

Around lunch time on Sunday 23 May 1943 sixteen Focke-Wulf 190s flew in low with their bombs and cannon fire causing fire, havoc and death. Their hotel received a direct hit.

16   Well Dug In

By the time the first anniversary of the move came round it was as if we had been in Malvern all our lives. Many of the problems besetting our daily existence had been solved.

Getting one's hair cut was one such problem, since the influx of some thousand odd heads of growing hair was grossly overwhelming Malvern's one barber's shop. Rowe, always concerned about his scientists wasting time on non-research activities, saw to it that TRE engaged its own barber. He was set up in the basement of one of the school houses where we could obtain a haircut with the minimum loss of the firm's time through the mechanism of a ten-minute appointments system.

Another innovation to save scientific staff from becoming bogged down with non-scientific tasks was the appointment of a number of retired army, navy, and RAF officers, one attached to each division, for the purpose of attending to all the odd administrative chores such as booking transport, obtaining rail warrants, chasing equipment orders, and so on. They were called divisional organizing officers, or DOOs. In the post-war world of government research they were to blossom into a professional administrative service: staffed by executive-grade civil servants and called Divisional Administrative Officers they had a supporting staff of clerical officers and assistants. Their wartime predecessors, however, had none of these advantages. They were equipped with nothing more than a desk, a telephone and enthusiasm. They were a mixed breed however, some appearing keen and efficient while others were regarded as 'Colonel Blimps'. Many of us already had good contacts in stores, transport and accounts and so had little reason to bother them.

Sweets were rationed and cigarettes were hard to come by which was reason enough for staff to slope off into town during the day in search of such scarce commodities. Such habits were an anathema to Rowe who therefore had no reason to discourage a member of his own office staff, one Arthur Wolleter, from dispensing cigarettes and chocolate from the superintendent's outer office early each morning. Arthur, who was an original Bawdseyite, had that knack given to few of being able to obtain supplies of rare commodities in time of scarcity, and furthermore without resorting to the black market. It was hardly surprising therefore that such a handy service which started on a purely unofficial and personal basis should rapidly escalate. There was a convenient room at the entrance to the gymnasium which was where the benign Arthur was allowed to set up shop with official blessing. Opening during the lunch hour, it went from strength to strength and soon developed into a general store, thereby providing a valuable service to the establishment.

Much building had taken place in the college grounds during the first year. Aside from the Senior Turf which remained inviolate, wherever virgin soil existed, buildings sprung up upon it. Principal of these was the canteen and main stores. On a site beyond the college campus a replacement for RPU, the production unit left behind north of Bournemouth, was erected. This was EU – meaning 'Engineering Unit'. It was far more extensive and comprehensive than RPU, and equipped to handle the very wide range of processes demanded by the innovative character of TRE's work. Also among the service buildings was a civil-defence control and training centre plus a number of associated firewatchers' huts.

Occupying a group of single-storey lab buildings was BBRL – the British Based Radiation Laboratory – which as its name implied was an outstation of MIT's Radiation Lab, of Boston, Massachusetts. Their staff were partly civilian scientists and partly uniformed technicians. One of their number, Lieutenant

Bob Doran, was attached to our group. He supervised many of the flight trials made in the Boeing.

* * *

Concurrently with the establishment getting organized and generally settling in at Malvern, the Telecommunications Flying Unit (TFU) had been going through much the same performance following their move from Hurn. Defford aerodrome which had been taken over was just eight miles from Malvern, but a considerable amount of work needed to be done before it was large enough to accommodate and operate all the aircraft brought up from Hurn.

For the first few months of occupation giant American earth-moving machines were seemingly as numerous as the aircraft. Vast mountains of earth were thrown up and seemed occasionally to move around like the sand of the Sahara desert. When the disturbed soil was not getting blown about in hot, dry weather it was making a sea of mud whenever it rained, and it rained plenty those first few weeks of late spring in 1942.

In spite of such tribulations, to say nothing of the problems of getting into the place and traversing its wide area (unless one was a regular visitor equipped with a permanent pass and one's own transport) it was an exciting place in which to find oneself. The diverse range of aircraft to be seen was of a Jane's almanac writ large. Top of the list for their size and aggressive power were the new super bombers – the Lancasters and Halifaxes which were being equipped with prototype H_2S sets; while gaining full marks for sheer beauty in performance were the Mosquitoes whose role as far as TRE were concerned would be as pathfinders equipped with Oboe.

Most in evidence was the ubiquitous Wellington bomber. Many different radar systems were given flight trials in this remarkable workhorse of a plane. Of the twin-engined fighter/bomber class there were Ansons, Blenheims and Beaufighters, the latter making an important contribution to the centimetre AI programme.

But for those of our own group nothing compared to our Boeing. Luxury indeed. Not for us the necessity to shin up through a tiny hatch in the belly of a fighting plane to crouch in close quarters to the equipment. We enjoyed armchair flying with our equipment spread liberally along a bench.

The more off-beat variety of aircraft was provided by the Naval Section. The Fulmers, Fireflys and Barracudas were reasonably normal unless one chanced to encounter them with their wings folded; but looking decidedly outdated in this age of the Spitfire were a number of Swordfish. These single-engined biplanes, although showing their age, had been steadfastly performing a wide range of tasks from reconnaissance to the dangerous role of torpedo bomber. There had been a programme to equip a proportion of them with 1½ metre ASV, hence their presence at Defford.

The oddest of the navy's collection was undoubtedly the Walrus, of which there was one at Defford. A most ungainly-looking biplane, it was actually amphibious, and in addition to its floats it had a pair of small wheels amidships and a tail skid. When it first landed on the Defford runway the CO had kittens and immediately ordered that the skid be replaced by a wheel. The navy might be the senior service but he was not going to allow anyone to scrape his runway!

The war was just about over when Defford had its first jet plane, a Gloster Meteor. We would watch in amazement to see the steepness of its climb and its speed in taking off. Frank Whittle's invention of the jet engine had not long become publicized and it was only then that we had an explanation of a strange occurrence a year before. It was while carrying out tests on the Firefly lock-follow radar from the window of House 8 that the scanner suddenly looked on an aircraft flying at some distance over the Vale of Evesham. Someone noticed the reading on the rate of change of speed indicator; it registered 600 mph. It was discounted as phoney – some equipment malfunction, for aeroplanes just did not fly that fast, or so it was then thought. But this, the first jet fighter, had been developed and put into production no more than twenty miles away in Gloucester.

* * *

By the summer of 1943 the powers that be presumably considered that TRE was now sufficiently tidy and respectable to allow the establishment to be graced by a visit from their Majesties King George VI and Queen Elizabeth. Although TRE was accustomed to receiving very important visitors, this particular occasion brought on an outbreak of management-inspired madness in its preparation.

Following the old army maxim, 'If it moves salute it, if it stays put paint it', a whole army of people were conscripted from the staff to make what were deemed the necessary cosmetic adjustments to the face of the establishment. Here there was no one to salute but no lack of objects to paint. Much of this effort fell upon the shoulders of the 'heavy gang'. They were the riggers whose principal job was the erection of aerial towers and suchlike, but they would always be called upon to shift anything heavy, hence their nickname. Their proud foreman was a small energetic character by the name of 'Chiefy' Francis who had led this vital team since the early days at Bawdsey. There is no record of what he said when told to put his men on to scrubbing the flagstone floor of the entrance hall and the groundfloor corridor of the Main Building. Meanwhile, for those needing aerial towers erected or heavy equipment moved, the war would have to mark time for a few days.

There was no limit to the madness; even doors were swapped around to improve the appearance along the royal route, and if anyone happened to have a newish doormat it was appropriated in exchange for a threadbare one. But the swapping business reached a bizarre extreme over the question of the humble toilet roll for the royal rest-room. It was thought that the legend: 'Government Property' which was printed on each sheet of the regular store-issue roll might offend royal susceptibilities. Accordingly a non-government replacement was hurriedly procured. Such minute concerns with appearance seemed out of place and time for the royal couple who during the blitz had been seen picking their way through the rubble to meet their stalwart subjects.

Neither was the Engineering Unit immune from these shenanigans. Here the apprentices had been busy crafting a splendid scale model of a radar scanner, silver plated and polished, and mounted on an ebony base.

Joe Morley, the chief foreman, viewed their efforts with some amusement and with tongue in cheek told them that upon it being presented to the King he would turn and hand it to his equerry who would pass it on to the royal bodyguard and so on back down the line of VIPs. With luck it would end up in the hands of the royal chauffeur who would dump it in the boot of the royal Daimler.

Many a true word – for on the appointed day it all happened almost exactly as Joe had predicted except that the person at the end of the line was none other than Joe himself. He was last seen outside the building looking for the royal chauffeur!

17 'Can You Do Nine Teas?'

One morning in April 1944 I had a message to report to Jimmy Atkinson's office in House 8. 'Ah Reg, you're to go home and pack enough clothing for three weeks and meet back here at two o'clock.' 'What's this all about?' I enquired. 'Just you be back here at two o'clock and you'll find out – oh, and by the way, don't forget your steel helmet.' (Those of us on firewatching squads or in the Home Guard were equipped with tin hats).

With a mixture of curiosity and alarm I took myself off home as I had been told. I was a little uneasy in one respect however, because at that time I was officially no longer in Jimmy's group but was in the course of moving over to Bill Burcham's group in the Preston lab. The Firefly project had failed ignominiously and Bill had taken the opportunity to grab me in order that I could do for AI Mark VIII what I had been doing design-wise for the Firefly system (Bill was now in charge of 10 centimetre AI systems, and Mark VIII was to be a large-scale production to follow Mark VII which had been the first centimetre AI in service). There had been a battle over my body, for naturally Jimmy was not going to allow his facilities to be liquidated without a fight, particularly since he was taking on important new work. The argument had been settled by Dee who considered Mark VIII was the more urgent. What was it that had cropped up that allowed Jimmy to grab me back?

Arriving back at Jimmy's office just before two o'clock, complete with tin hat and bag, I discovered that I was not alone. There were also Russel Aves, Arthur Cockroft, and two others from our original group plus a motley collection of others, scraped up from around the establishment – there were nine of us in all.

We all found ourselves a variety of seats round the room as Jimmy began his briefing. 'Do any of you know anything about Oboe?' he enquired. Not one responded. I glanced around. Here were nine of us, all with blank expressions, like tailor's dummies. It looks as if we have the right qualifications, I thought, there's nothing like total ignorance for starting a new job!

'Oh well, I guess you'll soon find out,' he responded, expressing a degree of pious hope. He then went on to explain that there were a number of vital targets along the French coast that were required to be neutralized before a 'certain operation was launched' (which was how he avoided using the word 'invasion' which we all guessed was not far off). Various bombing attempts had been made without success, and that included the US Air Force with their vaunted Sperry bombsight. We were given to understand that these targets were fortifications which needed to be pinpointed and destroyed before any landings could be made. It was therefore decided to use the Oboe system which for the previous eighteen months had been used successfully by Bomber Command for accurately bombing the Ruhr targets. However, it had been found that nothing like the theoretical accuracy necessary for this task was being achieved.

This was our brief therefore: to acquaint ourselves with details of the system on site, and then to effect a cure. Accordingly we were all to report to a 'Flight Lieutenant Davies at Dover', who would explain the system and the problems. Dover! – 'Bomb Alley'! No wonder we were told to bring helmets.

A Ford V8 shooting brake which could take six passengers was due to arrive from Transport Section in about half an hour; meanwhile Jimmy instructed Arthur Cockroft and myself to leave immediately with Russel Aves in his Morris 8. In next to no time we were speeding along the A40 towards London at all of fifty miles an hour. Arthur Cockroft was in front next to

Russel, while I settled down on the back seat with our three cases piled up next to me for company. It was about 6 p.m. as we sped down Western Avenue towards the heart of London. One cannot now imagine attempting to cross the centre of London at that time of day with any degree of facility, but this was 1944. 'Well Reggie,' called out Russel, 'you're the Londoner – which way do we go for Dover?' 'How the hell should I know,' was my not exactly helpful reply. The fact was I was a *North* Londoner and apart from the Kennington Oval we northerners saw no point in crossing the river; all the attractions from Buckingham Palace to Regent's Park Zoo were over on our side!

It was Arthur therefore who got busy with the maps from which he concluded we should head for the Elephant and Castle and eventually through to the Old Kent Road. The latter had the right sound about it and so we eventually found ourselves free of the built-up area and purring along the A2.

The light was fast receding as we motored down the hill to the centre of Dover town. It was 10 p.m. and double summer time. 'Well, chaps, which way do we go?' Arthur and I both shrugged our shoulders. Each of us thought the other knew. As it was, the only collective information we had was Jimmy's brief instruction: 'Report to Flight Lieutenant Davies at Dover'.

It seemed that the obvious place to start looking for the mystic Flight Lieutenant was at Swingate CH station just above us on the cliff top near Dover Castle, but here we drew a blank so we carried on along the coast road towards Deal. Soon it was quite dark but we ploughed on, enquiring at any place which had the faintest signs of a service connection which included an army command post and an AFS control centre where it was surprising I didn't get arrested as a spy since I had omitted to identify myself while enquiring as to the whereabouts of an RAF station.

A chance meeting with a bunch of erks merrily returning from an evening's drinking finally put us on the right road – a very narrow lane with high hedges, to be precise. At the top of a hill, finding ourselves in an inky dark void, we were about to despair when accompanied by a dim flicker of light a friendly voice enquired, 'Are you the gentlemen from TRE?' At last, our destination!

In the briefly lit guard-room we were told that Flight Lieutenant Davies had gone off duty but was expecting to see us next morning; meanwhile rooms had been booked for us at a hotel down in Deal. The watch was just going off duty so we were told that if we cared to follow their transport it would show us the way into town. But we were no match for the young WAAF driver of the great three-ton truck who drove with such confidence and zest that before Russel had a chance to get into second gear, the vehicle with its dim rear lights had disappeared into the darkness.

We eventually found the hotel which masqueraded under the grand-sounding name of The Regent or some such, which led us to expect something more imposing than the three-storey Victorian edifice in a deserted and somewhat run-down terrace. It had none of the appurtenances of a hotel *per se,* neither did we find it possessed public rooms worthy of the term. We were received by a young man who was tall, slim, and pasty in complexion. He had a suspicion of an accent which suggested he might be Polish. He was about to show us to our rooms when we tentatively broached the subject of food. We were aware it was fast approaching midnight but we had had nothing since lunch time. We were shown down to the kitchen where his sister obligingly brewed some tea and prepared some cheese sandwiches. The room was plain and well scrubbed in appearance but pleasantly warm from the large Ideal boiler burning away in the corner.

Having enjoyed our simple meal and learnt from the couple what it was like to be living within range of the German long-range guns near Calais which regularly shelled this strip of Kent coast, we were about to depart for bed when the sound of a vehicle drawing up outside announced the arrival of our colleagues. They had not got away until a full hour after ourselves, had taken a different route, had had a similar series of bizarre experiences in trying to find the elusive Flight

Lieutenant Davies, yet here they were almost exactly an hour after ourselves.

* * *

The mild-mannered Flight Lieutenant Davies was completely overwhelmed as nine untidily dressed civilians marched into his small office. In fact he was noticeably embarrassed at the thought of how he was to employ a posse of what he imagined (largely erroneously) to be 'brilliant young scientists' from the Mecca of radar research. 'We certainly have some problems,' he said, 'but I can't see at the moment how all of you can help us.' However, as a start he took out a series of technical manuals which he handed to us, and then proceeded to explain in broad terms what Oboe was all about.

It was a navigational-cum-blind-bombing system devised by A.H. Reeves seconded to TRE from STC Ltd. Like GEE it used a pair of geographically separated ground radar stations. These transmitted pulses to the controlled aircraft which in most instances was a high-flying Mosquito acting as a pathfinder. A 'transponder' unit in the aircraft retransmitted the received signals back to the ground stations where the distance and speed could be computed.

One of the ground stations was called the 'Cat', its function being to ensure the pathfinder maintained a constant range as it flew over the target area. This was accomplished by superimposing tone signals on the radar pulses which the pilot would hear as dots or dashes according to whether his track (which was an arc) was more or less than the set distance. When at the correct range the dots and dashes merged into a continuous tone.

The second ground station was the 'Mouse'. This operated in like manner to the Cat, but as well as sending a signal when the range measured corresponded to the intersection of the two arcs which pinpointed the target position, the Mouse station could also measure the plane's airspeed, and with the ballistics data of the bombs or flares to be dropped could compute and signal the moment of release to the navigator/bomb-aimer by a series of tone signals.

Having become acquainted with Oboe's Cat and Mouse game from our session with Davies we were taken on a conducted tour of the station. The system first became operational by Bomber Command at the end of 1942. Initially it was operated on 1½ metres using much existing equipment in order to get the system into service as soon as possible. This was followed by a Mark II system transmitting on 10 centimetres but again it was all put together at TRE by Dr F.E. Jones's division and became operational early in 1944. The Mark I and II systems were co-sited, sharing some of the control equipment, at Land's End, Swanage, Deal and on the Norfolk coast.

An advanced Mark III system had been developed and was being manufactured and installed by A.C. Cossor (who built the original CH receivers). It was designed as a multi-channel system capable of controlling several aircraft simultaneously. It also embodied many improvements gleaned from experience with Marks I and II. Undoubtedly once in service it would have been sufficiently adequate for the special task then in question, but unfortunately there were still many months of work to be done before it would be ready for service.

This then concluded our sight-seeing tour during which we had been most impressed with the Mark III system, but somewhat disenchanted with the Mark I and II gear having to be used. In some respects we were surprised it was producing the results then being achieved. Hits on the marshalling yards at Hamm, for example, were spectacular as shown in reconnaiss-ance photographs; and after all this was the kind of job it was designed to do, but pinpointing coastal gun emplacements was a whole different ball game, which is exactly why we had been brought in.

We had now gone as far as we could on this first session and the time had come to relieve the overburdened Lieutenant Davies of our presence (it was lunch time in any case). We had been given a good insight into the system and we now had the technical manuals with circuit diagrams to study. Meanwhile

Jimmy would be joining us later that day when, based on our impressions, a plan of action would doubtless be formulated.

Back in town for some lunch we took the opportunity to find a more inspiring place to stay. We discovered an eighteenth-century-style inn at the town centre which could accommodate us all and so we duly moved in. A greater part of the town centre was in ruins as a result of constant shelling. Apart from the little main street the place seemed largely deserted for presumably many of the residents had evacuated themselves to less fraught places inland.

That afternoon we wandered back and forth along the sea front, taking advantage of the desolation to discuss the implications of what we had learnt that morning without the risk of being overheard. It was then that we came across a tea room – it had seen better days even without Nazi intervention but it did appear to be operational. We all trooped in to the astonishment of its frail proprietor. 'Can you do nine teas?' enquired our spokesman. 'What's that?' he replied, not of very good hearing. 'April the nineteenth?'

We did indeed get our afternoon tea, even though it took some time to materialize. No matter, time was one commodity of which at that moment we had plenty. While waiting, the lads found stacks of glossy magazines including the *Tatler* and *London Illustrated News*. They were even older than those customarily found in a doctor's waiting room, but their rather dated pictures of town and country life before the war were mildly entertaining. Then one of our number noticed a familiar face among a group of top people at some social gathering – it was our *bête noir*, Wing Commander Derek Jackson (then plain 'Mr Jackson' according to the caption): the man who had just torpedoed our Firefly AI project!

* * *

We had got comfortably installed in our alternative accommodation and had eaten well. There was nothing to do until Jimmy arrived but to repair to the public bar where we commandeered their entire stock of stools and sat ourselves in line along the bar. We proceeded each in turn to buy a round of pints (I was not the only one to wonder how we would all be by the time the last caller was reached – we had the whole evening anyway). The conversation was quite jolly until one of our number, a Scot, came into unfriendly conversation with two of the locals – old salts who were undoubtedly put out because they couldn't get near their own local bar. One was positively vitriolic, accusing us of being a bunch of conchies[1] and telling us we should be out in the Western Desert. Furthermore they obviously wondered why nine healthy young men were not in khaki. Fortunately at that moment Jimmy arrived which gave us reason to retire gracefully and to avoid the consequences of exceeding the seventh pint.

We all followed Jimmy upstairs to the well-furnished and comfortable residents' lounge, where, succumbing to Jimmy's legendary charm, the landlord's wife was in the act of serving him with a plate of most appetizing sandwiches and a pot of hot coffee even though it was by now well after 10.30 p.m. We disposed ourselves around the room, still clutching our tankards with the remains of the rudely interrupted seventh round.

Jimmy had arrived hot-foot from London where he had been attending a meeting at the Air Ministry and notwithstanding the length and busyness of his day, he was ebullient and raring to go. (Jimmy was always ebullient and raring to go.) As for his troops, we were somewhat somnolent: the near three hours of steady drinking was taking its soporific toll. Jimmy's enthusiasm was contagious however, and gradually we slipped into gear, one by one, activated by his searching questions. Collectively we imparted our impression of the system and where it appeared at first glance to exhibit weaknesses. It was generally agreed that in practical terms there was not a lot that nine people could do here on the spot immediately. It was therefore decided that Russel, Arthur and myself should remain in Deal a further day to formulate a plan of action with Davies. As for the rest of the party, they were to return to Malvern the next day amidst a feeling of anti-climax.

That night there was a shell warning. We all got up and

stumbled around the corridors expecting to find a member of the hotel staff who would tell us what we should do and where we should go. None but our own selves were in evidence, neither did we hear any whines or crumps. With sleepy resignation we wandered back to our beds.

The next morning we three reported back to the Oboe site. While Arthur Cockroft in particular went through facts and figures in the technical manuals with Davies, I went around inspecting the display and control equipment. Together our findings were that a more precise quartz crystal master oscillator was needed, for the accuracy of all the distance and airspeed measurements was dependent on this item; and for my part I had observed that the display strobe control which was used to set and control the given distances was very coarse and potentially unstable. An improved method of control was needed. A programme of improvements which would have to be applied to all the station was then agreed with Davies and would be implemented as soon as the necessary material could be assembled. By midday we were on our way back to Malvern.

* * *

With regard to the quartz crystal oscillators it was the GPO Engineering Department who came to the rescue. Their research department at Dollis Hill, North London, had developed some extremely stable and precise quartz crystal assemblies. They were carefully ground and had a unique type of assembly (a quartz crystal's operation is significantly affected by the way in which the slice is held) which was vacuum-sealed in circular copper cans about three inches in diameter. Their circuit included a small degree of adjustment to facilitate the accurate setting of the oscillation frequency after each of the crystals had been installed. A precision master oscillator would be required for this process, one of which would be lent to us by Dollis Hill.

Meanwhile I had devised an improved strobe control. Instead of a single continuously variable control we replaced it for a multiway switch selecting coarse steps from a fixed resistor chain, together with a limited-range variable resistor for fine adjustment. The highest-grade components were to be used.

As soon as a batch of crystals had been made up at Dollis Hill and we at TRE had assembled a prototype strobe control, preparations were made to try out the planned modifications at the Deal station.

The original team of nine was now down to two – Russel Aves and myself, and so once again we were on the Dover road in Russel's long-suffering Morris 8. En route we had been obliged to call in at Dollis Hill to collect a batch of crystals and the test set and to be instructed in its operation. We had been somewhat taken aback when introduced to the master test oscillator. It was not the handy box as expected but a two-foot high rack of units requiring two people to lift it, and it was not without some difficulty that we were able to load it into the back of Russel's car.

As a result of these proceedings we were somewhat behind schedule and so we decided to make an overnight stop at Rochester (or were we actually in Chatham?). We found a hotel, but parking was out on the street. There was a police station nearby so it seemed a good idea to leave the car in their care overnight. The duty sergeant was a perfect stereotype – well built, mature, and with a bushy moustache. He was duly impressed with Russel's confidential mention of 'secret equipment' and readily agreed to the modest saloon being parked in their yard.

Thanks to the overnight stop we were on site at Deal bright and early. The efficient Flight Lieutenant had his lads ready on hand to assist us and so it took little more than an hour to effect the modifications. We then set up the test equipment, made the necessary checks, and set the Oboe crystal oscillator to its precise operating frequency. There were no snags and the whole operation was completed by lunch time. They would be carrying out a training run with a pathfinder aircraft that afternoon and if all went well the station would be used operationally that night. 'Well,' said the witty Russel as we drove back to Malvern, 'I hope they hit the right town tonight or we'll be for it!'

Footnote

1. Conscientious objectors

18 Countdown to D Day

The experimental modifications to the first of the Oboe stations at Deal (official name 'Walmer') having proved a success, preparations had been made to modify all the stations in the chain. The required number of kits which included the Dollis Hill crystals had been assembled, and over the course of several days, RAF radar mechanics from the various stations had come to TRE to collect the kits and be instructed in how to implement the modifications. When all the stations had been fitted out it would be my responsibility to visit each station in turn accompanied by a Pilot Officer from 84 Wing, Cambridge, who were responsible for the Oboe system, to check the conversions and to set the precise operating frequency of the crystals using the Dollis Hill equipment.

It was late in the afternoon of Friday 26 May, which had it not been wartime would be heralding the Whitsun bank holiday weekend, when the message came through from Wing for me to meet up with their man in Swanage as soon as possible. We had been having a spell of warm sunny weather and I had been looking forward to enjoying it on our Saturday rest day, but unfortunately for me it was not to be because 'very conveniently' TRE Transport happened to have a three-ton truck leaving for Swanage early that very morning.

It was a motley collection of bodies I joined that morning, some RAF and some TRE types. There was a distant air of urgency about this journey's preparations as the truck called at various groups' buildings to load equipment, including my own. From the fact that a significant proportion of men and material came from Dr Robert Cockburn's radio countermeasures division one felt that the big day was not far off.

The day was just perfect for a trip to the coast but not for sharing the back of a lorry with a load of electronics. The sun shone, the sky was blue, and the rolling downs were fresh in their late spring colours. But we were not there to enjoy nature and the fact that the roads were busy with traffic – military traffic – British and American, was a constant reminder that we were about the serious business of preparing for the greatest seaborne invasion of all time.

Arriving in Swanage I realized that it was two years almost to the day (24 May 1942; it was now 27 May) since we left. Not a lot had changed except that it had temporarily become an American colony. At the RAF mess I located the Pilot Officer I was to accompany. He was a likeable young man much my own age and I knew immediately that we were going to work well together. He quickly outlined our itinerary, a veritable Cook's tour from Land's End to the Wash, for which Wing had provided him with an RAF staff car and WAAF driver. We would kick off the next morning at the Swanage Oboe station. This was at Durlston Head near where the Dorset Country Park visitors' centre building now stands. It had the code name 'Tilly Whim' after the caves not far below in the cliffs. Meanwhile they had booked overnight accommodation for me at a place called Bon Accord not far from the front where out across the bay could be seen a multitude of shipping at anchor, doubtless awaiting the signal to set sail for the coast of France.

The operation at Tilly Whim that Sunday morning was both straightforward and successful. Our Pilot Officer friend was impressed and doubtless relieved to find the operation reasonably simple. It augured well for the pending expedition. We took an early lunch at the mess after which our car and WAAF driver were ready and waiting outside. We were to head west with the object of reaching Land's End that evening. As we travelled along from Dorset into Devon, wherever there was woodland there were allied troops with their equipment camped within. The sight was unforgettable; beneath the West

Country's leafy awning were vast armies of men and materials, tuned to a high pitch, waiting for the curtain to go up on the big show.

The long journey west was not made any shorter by finding that the Army had closed the road across Bodmin Moor. This necessitated a lengthy detour through Liskeard to the south. Nevertheless, although it was all but ten o'clock, thanks to double summer time the sun was only just setting as we drove down into Sennen Cove – our destination. Bathed in the evening light the scene was truly idyllic. The sheltered waters of the bay were lazily lapping the shore, calm and crystal clear, revealing a pebble-strewn sea bed. It was picture-book perfection, making our presence on wartime pursuits wholly unreal: surely the wrong stage-set for the play we were acting.

Our staff car drew up in front of one of the first of the stone buildings which lined the shore road. The little hotel whose front looked out across the cove displayed a sign which proudly proclaimed it to be a sixteenth-century inn. It happened to be the best hostelry for miles around and so it was hardly surprising that it had been taken over for the officers' mess. The advantage of being a civilian on these jaunts was that one was treated as an officer (whilst maintaining friendly contact with the other ranks). Hence I was provided with accommodation in the same delightful hotel as the Pilot Officer.

The next day we set off to carry out our appointed task at each of the two stations, namely Sennen and Treen, both within strolling distance of Land's End. Unfortunately we were to learn that we could operate only between the hours of six and nine in the evening. This was the free period between routine maintenance and training flights during daytime, and 'ops' over enemy territory at night.

There was hence nothing to do but take ourselves off during the day to a nearby beach where we lazed in the sun, threw the occasional stone at washed-up tin cans, and wished we had brought swimming togs rather than tin hats. If all this added to the phoney holiday atmosphere we had to remember that old army maxim: 'They also serve who only stand and wait'.

Indeed the climate and the ambience of this place were distinctly Mediterranean, and we had seen the succulent crop of sweetcorn which the radar mechanics had succeeded in growing in the sun-drenched soil around their workshop building.

We eventually completed our appointed task at Sennen and Treen, even though each working day had been limited to three hours by operational necessities, which lengthened our stay at Land's End. Next on our programme was a return visit to Deal, there being more than one station on that site to be dealt with. However, we had received a message that some additional components were urgently required there which would necessitate our calling in at Malvern en route. I received this information with mixed feelings for although a night back at home had its attractions I was sure that after all these days away there would be problems should the long-suffering Dr Burcham be aware of my whistlestop return.

There was no avoiding this arrangement however, and having enjoyed my night at home I was on site early next morning to sort out the requested items from the lab. Intending to keep a low profile I was no sooner through the gate and walking swiftly across the college grounds when a familiar voice hailed me from behind. Just my bad luck, it was Bill Burcham himself.

'Back at last Reg?'

'Er, not actually Bill, we've just stopped off for some bits and pieces.'

'You mean to say you're off again?'

'Afraid so Bill, we've got three more stations to do.'

Bill Burcham was not one for losing his temper but on this occasion he quietly blew his top. 'You're not to leave this site until you hear back from me,' he commanded as he strode off in the direction of Dee's office.

I sidled off to the lab and after sorting out the parts required at Walmer settled down to wait with a mug of tea. Meanwhile the question of my immediate future had reached the stratospheric heights of TRE's top management. Our Pilot Officer and his driver were not pleased. They were champing at the bit, anxious to get going. We did not have to wait long, however, for very soon word came down from above that I was to proceed as planned. Once again poor old Bill had lost the priorities battle.

Back at Walmer we set about our routines of checking and testing, operations with which we were both becoming adept. Suddenly the whole place seemed to come to attention – the boss man had arrived. This was Wing Commander Edward Fennessy. He was no desk-bound pen-pusher but one of the Bawdsey pioneers between 1935 and 1938. He finished the war as a Group Captain and after leaving the RAF became a leading figure in the telecommunications industry. He was knighted in 1975. He was now on an incisive tour of inspection and seeing us at work in the control room naturally wanted to know what we were about. Having heard our account he gave us the impression that he wasn't going to take anything at face value but would see what the operational results were before expressing an opinion. To use the time honoured RAF expression, he was not going to be 'flannelled'.

It now transpired that Walmer was short-staffed and so the CO took advantage of our presence and had my Pilot Officer friend hijacked on to his own strength. This left me to soldier on and to manage the east-coast stations on my own, a prospect which did not exactly win favour with the WAAF driver who was to carry on and transport me. Even with the uniformed Pilot Officer I had noticed a tendency for her to drag her feet at times and to show reluctance to accept orders. This situation was unlikely to improve now that she was left to transport a mere civilian, and a young one at that. I could hardly fail to notice a degree of coolness on her part as my equipment was loaded into her car the next day ready for our departure for Norfolk shores, therefore extreme diplomacy was going to be needed on my part.

* * *

There were two sites on the coast at Norfolk, Winterton and Trimingham. During our stay in this area I was to be based at Winterton, the principal of the two stations which was about ten miles north of Yarmouth. We arrived there at lunch time and I was driven straight to the mess. This was a beautiful old house standing in well-wooded grounds. We were met at the front door by the CO in person who before taking me into the dining room, first sent for his messing sergeant and instructed him to look after our driver and to see she got some lunch. I was soon to discover that this was quite typical of this outstanding officer and gentleman. It was not surprising therefore to find this station not only well run and efficient, but also a most happy one. He was a regular and before the war had been stationed in the Middle East with the rank of Wing Commander. In returning to home base he had reverted to the rank of Squadron Leader, as was the system. This he explained to me was the significance of the line: 'You get no promotion this side of the ocean,' in the popular song of the day, 'Bless 'em All'.

Trimingham was twenty miles further north near Cromer to where we travelled each of the days I needed to work there. It was the smaller of the two stations and was in distinct contrast to big brother to the south. Here the CO was a Flight Lieutenant of the wartime intake, and not having the experience of his professional senior at Winterton was obliged to operate strictly and self-consciously by the book.

The first morning we arrived I was greeted by the Flight Sergeant who showed me into the workshop. It was noticeably extra clean and tidy to the extent of it giving the impression that very little work had been done there. I asked him where I should put my equipment at which he apologized and asked if I minded standing by for a short while. At that moment the outer door opened and in came the Flight Lieutenant with his 'No. 1' – a Pilot Officer – close on his heels. Immediately the several radar mechanics who had been lounging about came quickly to attention beside their benches – an inspection was in progress.

On the second of the days spent at the Trimingham station I was taking the morning tea break with the men and women of the flight, which because it was mild and sunny was al fresco outside the technical buildings. There was an air of excitement, for someone had just heard the news on their workshop radio that the balloon had at last gone up – the Allied invasion force had landed on the coast at Normandy.

Suddenly the euphoric conversation was interrupted by the arrival in our midst of a large, bulbous American staff car. Even though covered in the regulation drab-green camouflage its chrome-plated brashness was subconsciously evident. The back door was flung open and out stepped a US Air Force Major. There was no mistaking him for other than American, even had he not been in uniform. He was tall, broad, had a sun-tanned complexion, and wore heavy horn-rimmed spectacles. Momentarily removing a fat cigar from between his lips he asked the nearest group of aircraftsmen to direct him to the CO's office.

As he departed in the direction of the admin. block, his driver got out of the car and then we all sat up to take notice. It was a sequence of a Hollywood film come alive. The girl was tall and attractive in a brassy kind of way; her long peroxide-blonde hair was displayed beneath the soft cap which was a feature of the American uniform. She wore an overabundance of make-up which did not go down well with the WAAFs in our company, and in their own thick grey regulation lisle stockings they coveted the sheer tan-coloured nylons (not then available in Britain) beneath her short, well-fitting, light khaki skirt. The more forward of the lads were soon gathered round her offering her cigarettes ('Sorry guys, I only smoke Camels'). They got little out of the encounter (the Flight Sergeant was beckoning them back to work anyway) except that they learnt that the Major was on a goodwill tour of British radar stations.

Back at Winterton for dinner that evening the Major was there as guest of honour at the CO's table. This caused much annoyance and complaint on the part of the station's two WAAF Section Officers who had been displaced from their customary seats at the top table. They weren't complaining at having to give way to the Major, it was the fact that he insisted that his driver sit beside him. 'Common tart – she shouldn't be here at all – there's a canteen for ordinary ranks', was typical of their vituperative remarks. The quietly spoken, hard working adjutant who kept the station's administrative machine at full pace merely smiled gently at their invective before returning to the serious occupation of supping his whisky, which was his usual relaxation after long, desk-bound days.

* * *

In due course my stint at Winterton was completed, and the time had come to pay my respects to the CO and to make my way back in the general direction of TRE. I was almost sorry to leave this happy station with all its friendly inmates. The staff car which for the past two weeks had been mine exclusively, giving me a feeling of great importance beyond my station, was soon to return to its home base which was the headquarters of 84 Wing at Cambridge. Here I would exchange the chauffeur-driven car for a humble railway warrant – third class!

And so with a certain feeling of achievement I boarded the train next day for the final leg of my grand tour – back to Malvern. Glad to be home, I was somewhat taken aback by my wife's suggestion that we join up with friends at TRE who were off for a holiday in the Lake District. True, the conditions for taking leave had recently been relaxed, but in my case at that instant it would be quite unreasonable to expect Dr Burcham, who for weeks had by events been denied my services, immediately to grant me leave.

Reporting back to him the next morning I tentatively broached the subject of leave and was most surprised when instead of the expected admonition he just gave a sigh of resignation, reflecting that perhaps another couple of weeks would be neither here nor there. This was so typical of the humanity that Bill Burcham always displayed.

* * *

By the time we were back from scrambling over Great Gable and Scafell Pike and getting thoroughly soaked in the process, June had all but ended. I was now more than ready to apply myself diligently to whatever task the patiently indulgent Dr Burcham had in store for me. But if a week is a long time in politics then a fortnight in wartime must surely be a lifetime. For while I had been away from the good doctor's clutches another emergency had arisen which was more urgent than AI or Mark VIII. It came as one word – Snorkel.

19 'Find those Snorkels!'

Hitler's U-boat fleet had been a constant menace throughout the war, accounting for serious Allied losses at sea. At the front line in this Battle of the Atlantic was the Royal Navy, whose ability to intercept the raiders had been improved with the introduction of the 10 centimetre Type 271 set, recounted in an earlier chapter.

In the air, Coastal Command had laboured for some time under the disadvantage of playing second fiddle to both Fighter and Bomber commands in the supply of equipment and technical aids. By 1944, however, they had been equipped with 10 centimetre ASV, and applying the planned patrol patterns developed by Professor Blackett's Operational Research team, the tide was beginning to turn in Britain's favour.

Although U-boats had been equipped with radio receivers designed to detect our radar transmissions, it had still been possible to catch them unawares, particularly at night when surfaced to recharge their batteries. The Leigh light was a significant contributor to the success of these nocturnal encounters.

Just as it was thought that the submarine threat was being overcome, a new development came to swing the balance back in the enemy's favour; it was their invention of the snorkel (spelt *Schnorchel* by the Germans).

It was a conceptually simple device consisting of a ventilation duct like a ship's funnel which allowed the craft to run its diesel engines while just submerged. Apart from the Navy's Asdic apparatus which, being a sound detector, operated only at a relatively short range, a snorkel-equipped U-boat was nearly impossible to detect by existing systems. It was now possible for them to move around with impunity – it was rumoured that one had even sailed up the Clyde.

Apart from the fact that the actual snorkel, being a small circular object, was difficult to detect by radar at any significant range, the sea itself, due to the waves, produces its own radar responses known as 'sea clutter'. This would cover the major part of the trace on the radar display, and to observe diminutive targets among the clutter was like looking for the proverbial needle in a haystack. To make matters worse it was then discovered that the Germans had developed a 'radar camouflage'. This was a dielectric coating on the snorkel, which had the property of absorbing the radar-transmitted energy, reducing significantly the amount reflected back to a radar receiver (predating the American Stealth bomber by some forty years).

The situation was therefore most serious, particularly now the seas beyond our shores were thick with Allied shipping keeping the invasion forces continually supplied.

Obviously this was a job for centimetre radar, but what kind of centimetre radar? 10 centimetres? 3 or even 1¼ centimetres? Should the aerial polarization be vertical or horizontàl? (i.e. whether the aerial dipole is vertical or horizontal). Were there any changes which could be made to the electronic circuits to improve the resolution? Answers to all these questions were needed to ensure a reasonable chance of detecting snorkels. There was one TRE group equipped to find these answers – Jimmy Atkinson's.

Just when the group had reached its nadir with the cancellation of the Firefly project some interesting and indeed perplexing phenomena were coming to light from divers sources concerning the propagation of radar signals. It had been observed that under certain weather conditions, targets at abnormally long distances were being detected. Because these responses were well beyond the range covered by the radar display, they would appear as ghost signals in the background.

This effect had been noted by RAF radar operators in India where coastal 1½ metre CHLs would occasionally detect craft at extreme ranges across the Bay of Bengal. The Americans operating in the Pacific had had similar experiences; there was the notable occasion when a whole gamut of ghost signals appeared on their screens without their realizing that they were due to a Japanese task force approaching the Aleutian Islands.

If nothing else, the latter case showed that we needed to know about the climatic mechanism that caused ultra-shore wave signals, which are normally propagated in a straight line, to follow the earth's curvature, hence affording communication beyond the normal limit of the horizon. This is the effect which occasionally causes interferences with television pictures, particularly for those in coastal regions, from foreign stations normally too far away to be received. An understanding of the phenomenon, from when it first became evident, would have allowed one to avoid or exploit its effect, so a programme was drawn up to study all the facets of anomalous propagation, particularly at centimetre wavelengths.

Hence it was that at the time Jimmy Atkinson and Bill Burcham were having a tug-of-war over my body (and I was being despatched on Oboe anyway), Jimmy's group were selected for this work. It was proposed that a series of centimetre sets be assembled for trials somewhere on the coast. Since the purpose of the tests was to investigate the effects of climate, the Met. Office were to co-operate in the programme and advise on a suitable region for the tests.

The site chosen was an experimental radar station belonging to the Admiralty, who were also interested in these investigations. It was at the summit of the Great Orme at Llandudno, which looked out across the Irish Sea. It was an ideal site, for not only were all the necessary services available but seventy miles out across the sea was the Isle of Man. At this distance its highest point, the 2,034 foot high peak of Snaefell, was significantly below the horizon, which from the top of the Orme was just over thirty-two miles. Under normal conditions therefore it would be out of sight of our radar. It was to be the

Met. Office's contribution not only to forecast, but to log the
weather conditions from day to day over the whole wide area,
awaiting the time when radar contact with objects well beyond
the horizon might occur. It was hoped this might include
Snaefell.

Since all the three services had an interest in the subject of
anomalous propagation, a well-integrated inter-services *ad hoc*
organization came spontaneously into being. In addition to the
Admiralty the Army came into the picture represented by the
Signals Research and Development Establishment, who had
been developing a 5 centimetre pulse-modulated radio-
telephone system. They had set up a trial link across Cardigan
Bay between Aberdaron (about fifty miles south of Llandudno)
and Fishguard, mainly for the purpose of studying the
propagation at this wavelength. The results of this work were
very relevant to the TRE programme, just as in return TRE's
findings would be useful to SRDE. Their 5 centimetre system
was to provide General Montgomery with a direct (and secret)
phone link with Churchill and the Chiefs of Staff in Whitehall
throughout Operation Overlord – the Allied invasion of Europe.

A most beneficial outcome of the SRDE connection was the
supply of useful manpower from a detachment of the Royal
Engineers. Equally as valuable as their sheer muscle power was
their experience in handling vehicles and plant in the field.
Whereas it would take at least three, sometimes four, of our men
together to start one of the large diesel electric generator sets, it
would take only one of these beefy army fellows to swing the
handle while a colleague kicked the bar to close the valves.
To watch these intrepid men with one of their large towing
vehicles (a Matador which came complete with power winch)
calmly backing a trailer onto a narrow shelf of rock at the cliff
edge, the best part of 700 feet above the sea, gave one a sense of
admiration tinged with fear. If a bulldozer was required the
army would conjure one up in a trice – Jimmy was fascinated
with what bulldozers could do and later would have the
opportunity to employ one.

The multi-way exchange of information and assistance

between all the parties in this venture particularly applied to TRE's association with the Met. Office. The quantity and speed of meteorological data required during the period of the trials were extending the abilities of the existing instruments. Here Jimmy's group were able to suggest and to implement improvements. The operation and tracking of radiosondes was a case in point.

Of the various problems in the field of meteorology unconnected with the propagation trials which came to Jimmy's notice, one was the need to determine the thickness of cloud cover over an airfield. Jimmy was sure that centimetre radar could provide the answer. An experiment was set up outside the lab, needing no more than a half-hour to assemble the necessary equipment, using a packing case for shelter and placing a 3 centimetre dish on its top facing directly upwards. As soon as heavy cloud conditions developed, convincing responses were obtained on the cathode-ray tube installed in the lab from which the height and thickness of the cloud cover could be measured. Within a day or so of the results being reported, the RAF sent a couple of WAAF radar operators to act as observers and to log measurements for a few days. Such was the pace at which projects could take off in wartime.

And so from a single major programme a whole range of subsidiary projects and experiments was spawned, all with a spirit of friendly co-operation amongst potentially rival organizations. Much of the success of these proceedings were undoubtedly due to a regular application of the Old Pals' Act.

When the snorkel problem raised its ugly self from beneath the waves, the obvious choice for the investigation was Jimmy's group. Not only did they have the necessary expertise but they were camped in the ideal place for trials, plus the fact that on Great Orme's Head they were guests of the Admiralty, who were concerned as much as the RAF with the task of searching out snorkels.

This was the situation as I was arriving back from my Oboe safari. In addition to the centimetre equipment already on site for propagation experiments, a number of additional sets, each operating on different centimetre wavelengths and with different aerial systems, were required. Each set would be installed in the ubiquitous trailer for transportation and operation at the site, together with power distribution cables, field telephones, and stand-by supplies. Jimmy was insisting that the best person to implement the provision and assembly of all this equipment was myself. Such was the degree of priority given to the snorkel programme that I found myself directed back to Jimmy's group to take on this ambitious programme of construction.

The snorkel project was a mansized job to get my teeth into, and for many weeks I seemed to have taken up residence at EU. My best friends were the welders, fitters and carpenters, who were busy with the construction work on our series of trailers, each of which needed major additions or adaptations.

But the facilities and expertise of EU were well up to the task and one by one the various trailer sets were made ready, tested out and despatched to Llandudno.

A significant proportion of our group were obliged to spend long periods at Llandudno engaged in taking countless signal-strength measurements day after day and then analysing the results. It was boring and uncomfortable work not helped by the strength of the wind encountered atop the Great Orme, a discomfort quotient greatly multiplied when accompanied by torrential rain. Some compensation was provided, however, by the discovery of a scientist-friendly hotel down in the town whose management were not put out by irregular work schedules nor by the numbers, which frequently fluctuated.

Come the autumn Skinner, Curran, and Aves among others quietly disappeared from the scene – they had been on the mysterious 'October List'. 'October List?' one would enquire, only to discover that if one knew not what it meant one was not permitted to know. But the truth was that they were part of the British contingent crossing the Atlantic to join the Manhattan Project, set up to develop the atomic bomb – a race against time lest Germany got there first.

As the months went by the group amassed a considerable

volume of data related both to the detection of snorkels and to establishing an understanding of the mechanism by which anomalous propagation occurred. The meteorological condition leading to the anomaly is known as 'temperature inversion'. This is when the air temperature which normally decreases as the height increases becomes reversed. The resulting air-density distribution effectively forms a duct parallel to the earth's curvature through which centimetre radio waves can travel, instead of as normal in a straight line when they would be lost beyond the horizon. While within a duct system the signals could travel seemingly great distances, just like voices through a tunnel compared to those across an open field.

From the acquired data it appeared that there was correlation between the transmitted wavelength and the effective ceiling of a duct. Furthermore the results indicated that from the top of the Great Orme at the wavelengths we were dealing with we could well be too high to be within the effective region of ducting. To check this prognosis it was decided to site one of the trailer sets as near down to sea level as possible. A suitable spot was a beach at nearby Morfa but the 3 centimetre set to be used had its aerial dish mounted on the trailer roof some ten feet above ground. At this juncture Jimmy's expressed fascination with bulldozers (going back to the long winter nights of 1940 when he conceived the construction of a giant radio telescope dish carved out of the ground by bulldozers) came to the fore. Here at last was a genuine use for one, and furthermore the army were at hand only too pleased to oblige. Accordingly a deep trench was dug above the normal high-water level into which the trailer was towed.

In this situation some valuable measurements were made throughout the summer months after which TRE Transport Section were instructed to tow the trailer back to Malvern. Unfortunately the autumn high tides got there first, filling the trench and submerging the trailer to about three inches above bench level. To make matters worse, our men had prepared for the journey by removing all the equipment from the bench top and laying it out on the floor. When the outfit finally arrived back at TRE, there was a distinct high-water mark round the interior walls and on the floor, saturated with sand and salt, a now useless set of electronic units.

At the same time – the end of 1944 – the majority of our mobile equipment, including the precious diesel electric generator sets, was brought back to Malvern for the winter and parked in the transport field. During that season just ended our Royal Engineer friends had taken these generator sets one by one back to their base workshops to be serviced. They were now in first-class running condition. Upon their arrival in Malvern Jimmy instructed Transport to drain the radiators since the sets would not be required again before spring, but the Transport Officer just laughed, suggesting that we were worse than women for changing our minds. He therefore insisted on filling their radiators with antifreeze. Unfortunately way back down the line of stores supply the antifreeze provided was of the wrong genre – it was the kind intended to treat aircraft oil for arctic service; its ability to prevent water freezing was nil. To compound this misfortune the winter of 1945 was particularly hard, with the result that scores of valuable vehicles of all kinds parked in the field sustained cracked engine blocks. In the case of our diesel generators the fissures were almost wide enough for one's fingers. For the users of this mobile equipment it was as well the war ended that spring.

Neither did the end of the war come too soon for the snorkel problem, for as 1944 came to its close we were no nearer a solution to a satisfactory system of detecting them by radar. A whole series of tests had been carried out in conjuction with the Navy, who had provided a submarine fitted with a dummy snorkel. At least an optimum arrangement had been established from the results of the tests with all the alternative choices of wavelength, aerial systems, etc. With the best of the systems the mock-up snorkel had been located and tracked reasonably well, but we were well aware that our observers were experienced scientists, working under favourable conditions, and with a good idea of where and when to look for the prey.

For a cold radar observer however, cooped up for some hours

in a Coastal Command Sunderland or Liberator, staring into a six-inch PPI display, what chance would he have of locating an isolated blip amongst a background of sea clutter as the plane covered a wide expanse of ocean? It was a tough nut to crack and it was hardly surprising therefore that thoughts were beginning to turn in the direction of infra-red technology.

20   The Twilight of the Gods

The war in Europe ended on 8 May 1945, appropriately designated 'VE Day'. The events of the preceding months, occurring at a gathering pace, were to build up to a grand finale – the death of Hitler and the final collapse of the 'Thousand Year Reich.' It was the last scene of a grand opera – a true-life Wagnerian epic.

The Allied advance in the west had, during the autumn of 1944, lost its momentum and Montgomery's attempt at a breakout in the north was to end in the disaster of Arnhem. Just before Christmas Hitler made a last attempt at a counter-offensive with the object of reaching Antwerp, but the initial thrust from south of Aachen had covered a mere fifty miles into the Ardennes before it was arrested and contained by the Americans. The resulting Battle of the Bulge was bitterly fought out in the extreme cold of that same January which had wreaked such havoc among the engine blocks in TRE's transport field.

Towards the end of March the British, and further south the Americans, secured crossings of the Rhine and by April both the British and American forces were well into Germany, pushing their way against a demoralized German army now unable to stem the tide. This same month, pleasantly warm with alternate sunshine and showers ('good growing weather,' said the man in our neighbourhood ironmonger's shop), the first of our two sons was born, and on 15 April the news came over the radio of the death of President Roosevelt. It was received with surprise and disbelief. His place in the Oval Office was taken by an energetic little man from Independance, Missouri, called Harry Truman.

'Harry who?' we asked each other, for Roosevelt had been such a gigantic figure that nobody had ever got round to knowing who was Vice-President.

Throughout all these months Bomber Command had continued to pound the major cities of the Reich by night, now joined by the US 8th and 15th Air Forces who added their weight by day. The Americans had suffered grievous losses in their initial period of daylight operations in 1943. Now they had the long-range Mustang fighters for protection. In any case, as one month succeeded another in 1945 the Luftwaffe became increasingly ineffective as their forward airfields were overrun by the advancing ground forces. Depleted by the effect of the bomber offensive on the nation's productive capacity, the increasingly impotent Luftwaffe no longer reached the west of England, but for London and the South East death still rained from the sky. It came mysteriously and silently until a powerful impact made its deadly presence known. Here with Hitler's vaunted V2 the age of the rocket had arrived.

Now that all the Allied armies were on the move and the Germans' ability to resist was noticeably crumbling, it was not unnatural that at TRE one began to have the feeling that our work was done – the vast Allied war machine was freewheeling to victory. True, our own group was still wrestling with the snorkel problem, and many at the establishment were turning their attention to the war in the Far East. Our trials at Llandudno had continued throughout the winter and into the spring, albeit on a reduced scale.

Sometime during this period Jimmy had been away touring the United States. It was an exploratory journey quite unconnected with snorkels and anomalous propagation, the purpose being to become acquainted with what the Americans were now doing in the field of guided missiles.

During the autumn of 1944 Jimmy had had a visit from Lord Cherwell, accompanied by an important-looking army general in uniform. Cherwell had persisted with his rocket developments and now some vestige of a guided-weapons programme was underway. Since the basis of the guidance was to be a lock-follow radar, we of the ill-fated Firefly lock-follow system had been lined up as presumed experts.

Having returned from his prodigious excursion visiting the various American groups (mainly aeronautical firms) working on these projects, Jimmy called the group together to report on his expedition and to outline the proposed programme should the group take it on, for apparently the choice was ours. It was a lively meeting which followed his exposé of what he had seen and learnt; he was at pains to acquaint us with what would be involved in such a project, and what would be expected of us should we accept the job. We all had mixed feelings, torn between the prospect of an exciting new undertaking and the obvious stresses of a highly political venture. Nothing could be politically higher than a project connected with Lord Cherwell – Churchill's own scientific adviser – which was to ignore the Prof.'s reputation for being involved with way-out schemes. After much discussion and on a very close vote the group elected to continue as they were.

As to those turning their attention to the war with Japan, already a new word had entered the lexicon – 'tropicalization'. Equipment which had earlier been sent out to India, designed for operation in our own temperate climate, was proving quite unsuitable for the tropics. As far back as 1943 various bodies had been engaged in solving these climatic problems, and a group under Schuler, who had joined TRE from the pre-war radio firm E.K. Cole, was set up to develop and provide means of testing components and equipment under simulated tropical conditions.

In preparation for the post-European war phase, volunteers had been sought from TRE staff, both technical and administrative, to staff an outstation based at Bombay, in charge of which was to be one of TRE's division heads, Dr Denis Taylor. A great quantity of equipment and spares was to be shipped out, and to withstand the long seaborne journey through tropical waters a range of special containers were designed, appropriately called 'tropicans'. Material packed into these was reputed to be immune to all hazards including being dropped from a great height. A sufficiently large quantity had been ordered but after some weeks had passed it was feared that the contractor was likely to be late on delivery. Accordingly a duplicate order was placed on an alternative firm, but then the original contractor put on a spurt and both consignments arrived almost simultaneously. A huge mountain of tropicans rose up near the main stores quite the size of a semi-detached pair of houses and thanks to a certain bomb which ended the war with Japan several months later, the size and shape of the heap had by then hardly changed.

By the end of April the Americans had met up with the Russians at a little place called Torgau, after which Berlin was to find itself in the jaws of the feared Russian pincer. Clearly the days of the Third Reich were numbered. It was afternoon and must have been 1 May when the radio programme was interrupted by a news flash – we caught our breath. 'Hitler is dead, Hitler is dead.' The message was brief, the newsreader's voice slow and distinct, but those three words repeated constantly for the rest of the afternoon were all we needed to hear – the detail could and did come later.

And so it was the free world celebrated VE Day, Churchill in a broadcast message declared 8 May a national holiday and the whole country went on a spree. In Malvern a bonfire was lit up on the hill – the Worcester Beacon – while in the town the beer flowed and there was spontaneous dancing in the streets. As for ourselves, having a month-old-baby, an early evening visit to the town was as much as we prudently allowed ourselves. We chose principally to celebrate with friends at home, and to mark the occasion in a way I thought most appropriate after the years of blackout: we rigged up some lights in old biscuit tins and floodlit the house, which being on the edge of Malvern Common could be seen for some distance.

The following months at TRE were like a game of musical chairs – everywhere was change and everywhere were people on the move. The Far East contingent departed for India, while another parcel of volunteers departed for Germany. The latter were scientists on loan to an organization designated SIGESO which was set up to investigate and report on German wartime scientific and technical developments.

For those of us under thirty there was now a whole new experience – the hustings; the 1945 General Election was upon us. Although there seemed to be a general desire for a brave new world not inhibited by old-guard administrations the ultimate result came as a great surprise to most.

When the Potsdam conference resumed (it had momentarily been adjourned pending a change in the British government), 'Uncle' Joe Stalin had two new boys facing him across the conference table – President Truman and Prime Minister Attlee. At this particular moment in time the wiry little President of the United States must have had the winning card tucked away unobtrusively in his pocket, for in little more than a week later came the earth-shattering event which ended the war with Japan and changed the world for all time – Hiroshima.

21   The Russians are Coming

Now that all war was finally over, movement was the name of the game at TRE. Those who had been on loan from firms, universities, the Post Office, BBC, or wherever were due to return from whence they had come. Service personnel were now counting the days until demobilization. A proportion of uncommitted staff were looking for pastures new, encouraged by an abundance of attractive offers now in evidence from firms. Meanwhile those with no immediate necessity nor desire to move on were naturally anxious to learn what future if any there might be at TRE.

Amongst those moving on was Chief Superintendent A.P. Rowe, who had been appointed Deputy Controller of Research and Development at the Admiralty. Before leaving he made a point of coming round the labs to thank us all personally and to say goodbye. His place was taken by Dr Lewis, who had been his deputy. His term of office would be comparatively short, however, for a year later he became Director of Canada's nuclear research establishment at Chalk River.

Within our own circle, Dee and Atkinson were off to Glasgow University where, together with Curran, back from the States, they joined the department of nuclear physics, which had now become the most important field of research. Dee had a singular lack of confidence in the ability of his now ageing motor car to make the journey to Scotland, the most exacting part of the long journey being the ascent of Shap Fell – no mean task in pre-M6 days. Jimmy, true to his fashion and who was following up the next day, provided Dee with a number of tins of the notorious

179

cellulose enamel, telling him, should he break down, to paint a suitable sign in the road. Jimmy, upon seeing it, would then expect to find him at the next pub down the road. We were not told what colour the enamel was but we doubted it was red!

Some months after Dee and Atkinson had left for Glasgow, Dr Skinner arrived back from Berkeley looking healthily tanned and half his age – the weather and food of California had obviously been beneficial. The government had announced that Britain's new Atomic Energy Research Establishment was to be at Harwell, and Skinner, together with Donald Fry (who in the 1960s was to be Director of the Winfrith Atomic Energy Establishment) were now back in Malvern on a recruiting exercise for staff for the new establishment.

One of the most important tasks for TRE now was to adapt wartime radar – particularly centimetre radar – to the needs of civil aviation. The six years of war had accelerated the development of aircraft of all kinds; the age of worldwide flight was about to dawn. London was to have a new airport in succession to Croydon: a hitherto unknown place called Heathrow! It was near to London and had a particularly long runway built during the war to take the heaviest of bombers. By all accounts it was a logical choice.

The person best equipped to lead the development of radar for civil aviation was John Duckworth, whose division had already been concerned with airfield and air-traffic control problems during the war. The summit of their achievement had been the creation of the mighty AMES 70 system. This was a complex mobile ground radar and air-combat control system which, following in the wake of the invasion forces, controlled the operations of the Tactical Air Force. It was a veritable travelling circus complete with a 'big top' to house the whole paraphernalia of a military flying control operations room when on station. On the move it became a vast convoy of road vehicles which followed the invasion forces on their juggernaut progress across France and into Germany. The techniques of this and other similar systems developed for the RAF were readily adaptable for civil use, but a degree of international co-operation was essential.

Accordingly PICAO – the Provisional International Civil Aviation Organization – was set up to co-ordinate the development of navigational systems, air-traffic control measures, and fare structures on a worldwide basis. This organization was to spawn a whole gamut of international conferences, *ad hoc* meetings and demonstrations. With the United States, Britain was in the van of this burgeoning movement.

These prospects excited me, particularly the chance to partake in the development of a high-resolution radar to monitor aircraft movements on the ground. Experimental work had taken place during the war for Bomber Command, who had expressed the need for a runway-clearance indicator. Anticipating a degree of congestion at post-war civil airports in marshalling aircraft landing and taking off in rapid succession, there was call for an Airfield Surface Movement Indicator – ASMI for short.

This project, which was one of a number of airfield control radars, was the responsibility of K.E. (Ken) Harris, who led one of the four groups which comprised the Duckworth division. The main project for the Harris group was ACR (Airfield Control Radar). This was a long-range radar operating on what is known as the secondary radar principle by which each aircraft carries a 'transponder' – a receiver which retransmits the radar pulses back to the ground stations in the manner of wartime IFF. The received signal is hence much stronger than that of a straightforward echo and the range covered proportionately greater. This radar would be a development of that used in the war but with an important new feature – a sophisticated identification system.

An airfield control radar at a major airport would need to be capable of dealing with large numbers of aircraft simultaneously – the return signal from each must have a unique identity corresponding to the plane's call sign. The solution being developed by the group involved a system of tones surperimposed on the returned radar pulses which would be decoded by a large bank of active tone filters. In the days of valve technology to accomplish such a complex system economically was a notable achievement.

I was hence able to get a transfer to Ken Harris's group and formed a partnership with Gwynne Court, who had previously been on H2S. Together we took on the job of developing ASMI, a project for which we were both well equipped.

To get the project going without delay we scrounged a set of 3 centimetre H2S equipment, complete with scanner, and set about modifying it. The Harris group occupied what was then the Grundy Library in the Main Building which from its first-floor situation looked out over the campus towards Bredon Hill.[1] The scanner was set up on a platform in front of one of the two mullioned windows, and in a very short time we had obtained some very convincing PPI pictures of the terrain below and beyond, from which many of the topographical features could be identified.

A proportion of the group were RAF radar mechanics on attachment with a Flight Lieutenant in charge. Their occupation was mainly conducting trials on the ACR set, which had been set up on Defford airfield. Concurrently work was proceeding in the lab on the tone decoder equipment and before long each of the group's projects was in a suitable state for demonstration. It was not long therefore before we were besieged by interested parties from many parts of the globe.

The Americans and Canadians were well in the fore, since both had been close partners during the war. The latter, when seeing the ACR equipment set firmly on the ground at one corner of Defford airfield, remarked that it would be of no use in one of their Canadian winters under ten feet of snow. Our man smartly replied that this hardly mattered for he couldn't see aircraft taking off and landing in ten feet of snow!

The French representatives when they arrived looked most out of place. The two dark, swarthy characters came dressed in black leather blousons, giving the impression that they had come on bicycles. Looking like members of the Resistance (which they probably had been), a colleague thought they might be as handy with explosives as with an oscilloscope!

The occasion least forgotten, however, was a visit from the Russians. Within the group we seldom had much advance notice of visits, and so it was when we arrived one morning and were told to expect a party of Russians that day. It was well before Churchill's notable Fulton speech, after which the Western world was to regard the Soviets with suspicion. But at TRE the one-way traffic in technical information and material when we were supposed to be allies had long made us suspicious of the Stalin regime. We all made up our minds therefore that we would tell them as little as possible.

They arrived mid-morning, the party consisting of two Red Army officers in uniform and a dour civilian from the Soviet Trade Mission in London. I was manning the ASMI equipment where the scanner was rotating on its mounting in front of the window, indicating that it was all working. Seeing this, the senior of the two officers jumped up on to the platform to have a look; he was duly impressed at what he saw on the PPI display. Glancing at the scanner, he enquired: 'This is 3 centimetres, yes?' Now, if one is anxious not to give too much away one assiduously avoids quoting figures. So what was I to do about such a direct question as to the wavelength we were using? Should I lie, or should I try to be vague. It all depended on how much I thought he knew about radar. Since he'd quoted the correct figure I decided he really knew and so I found myself lamely saying 'Yes.'

By the time my demonstration had come to its close he had solicited a number of pertinent facts and figures concerning the system by his clever questioning. Each of my replies had been noted down in a little book together with my name which I was obliged to spell out for him, but when he said: 'And what are your initials?' I thought he'd gone too far and gave him a look which as much as said it. He sensed my annoyance and so as a peace offering he reached into his breast pocket and took out a visiting card which he handed to me. It read 'Lieutenant Colonel Stefan Stevanov, Red Army' – I gave him my initials. Doubtless all this information together with my name (and initials!) would have finished up in a GRU file deep in Moscow vaults.

If our Russian visitors were not trained spies they certainly acted as if they were. Although they had seen all we had to show them that morning, they were back in the afternoon to have another look at the tone decoder – hardly surprising, it was unique. So while the Major went through the decoder circuits with Gwynne Court, Lt. Col. Stevanov joined me and a colleague up on our platform. His approach was friendly, for he began by mildly deriding us over the result of a football match the previous day when Moscow Dynamos beat Arsenal at Wembley (it had surprised us that Russians could play football at all, let alone beat England's top team). To add insult to injury the match had been played in fog, which amused the Russian, who laughed, suggesting that Arsenal might have done better had they been equipped with our ASMI radar.

Having enjoyed the joke at our expense he caught sight of a telescope of mine (it had originally belonged to my grandfather) which I had been using to identify our targets. Without saying a word the Lieutenant Colonel opened out the telescope, knelt down at the window and continued to spend a long time surveying each building and area of the college grounds in detail (funny I thought, grandfather used to call it a 'spy-glass').

Having witnessed this theatrical performance we were further taken aback when he took the two of us to one side, and opening out a sheet of paper asked us if we could help him. To our amazement we saw that he had been compiling a family tree of the division, with John Duckworth's name at the top and below columns of names comprising the four groups. There were of course gaps which he was asking us to complete, as well as confirming locations. It was as absurd as it was blatant, but smiling inwardly to ourselves we gladly obliged since he was not to know that at that time staff were continually leaving and the composition of groups was changing by the week. By the time his information got back to Moscow it would be meaningless.

The three of us rejoined the others, who were just completing their session with the decoder. Court then asked them if there was anything else they would like to see before leaving. At this the three Russians held a lengthy and animated discussion in their own language, after which one of them asked if it was possible to have a set of circuit diagrams of the decoder. We were all shocked at such presumption, but Gwynne Court without hesitation just smiled and pointing to his notebook he was holding replied that the system was so new that we only had what was recorded in our lab notebooks. It was a masterstroke on his part for in actual fact the cupboard standing just behind us was full of fresh prints. Never had the group been so well provided. The reason was that the squad of RAF radar mechanics attached to the group had been at a loose end awaiting their demob. To occupy them Flight Lieutenant King, their officer in charge, had put them on properly drawing out all the circuit diagrams.

The day the Russians came was a most incredible experience. What intrigued us was the unashamed openness in the gathering of information. It was made so obvious that we thought they were either just acting the part expected of them or taking us for simpletons. Or perhaps it was they were merely intellectual vacuum-cleaners trained to suck up information on anything and everything irrespective of its relevance or value.

* * *

Shortly after the visit from the Russians, the ASMI equipment was made ready for its transfer to Defford airfield for trials. The riggers had found us a fifty-foot wooden lattice tower to support a purpose-built cabin which would house the scanner, transmitter and receiver units. The cabin was about an eight-foot cube with perspex windows all round. In order that the scanner could have a downward view of the airfield the windows were at the lower half of the cabin walls, which made it look as if the cabin had been installed upside down. It was erected to one side of the airfield close to one of the huts wherein we installed the display and remote control equipment.

It was as well that the equipment up the tower required only occasional attention since the agility and nerve of a trapeze artist was required for the ascent and entry to the cabin through a trapdoor in the floor. This lofty perch however rewarded the intrepid climber with a fascinating bird's eye view of the aircraft taking off and landing, while on *terra firma* the modified H_2S display clearly showed the pattern of Defford's three intersecting runways complete with their lines of runway lights. Not only could one follow the movement of aircraft taking off, landing, and moving round the perimeter track to and from their dispersal areas, but the presence of motor vehicles and even pedestrians was clearly evident.

It seems that it was all of twenty years before ASMI was installed at Heathrow by Decca Radar. It was to serve the airport until 1989 when it was replaced by a new system produced by Thomson-CSF. The development of Airfield Control Radars (ACRs) was taken up by A.C. Cossor who, as I mentioned earlier, were responsible for the very first radar receiver for CH in 1937. Their first model to go into commercial service (ACR6) was at Heathrow in 1955. Many airports, both at home and abroad, were equipped with Cossor ACRs in the succeeding years.

*   *   *

Come December 1945 the India contingent arrived back, having been away hardly more than six months. Nobody knew at the time TRE's Far East enterprise was planned that in two violent flashes the war with Japan would be ended. Overnight the Bombay unit was redundant with hardly any of the precious tropicans opened and unpacked. But none regretted it now that all war had finally ended.

Now we were into 1946 – the first full year of peace – and TRE was once more on the move. Not far this time – about half a mile up the road to take over the premises of HMS *Duke* now the navy had departed. In many ways it was an ideal site with buildings more substantial than the Worth Matravers huts and superior in layout to any the establishment had endured throughout the war.

At long last the college was able to return to its own home. There was of course a monumental amount of restoration work to be done, which was far from complete at the time of the school's return in September 1946. But one feature of the college was as the staff and boys had left it – the Senior Turf. Rowe had seen to it that his promise was kept.

For TRE 'the Duke' was to be their final stop. In due course ADRDE moved down from Pale Manor to form an integrated establishment, which became known as the Royal Radar Establishment. Then, when the Heath government embarked upon a rationalization exercise in the early seventies, they were further combined with SRDE, who were moved up from Christchurch. Now as the Royal Signals and Radar Establishment (RSRE) they are there to this day, and within the grounds can be seen the now ubiquitous aerial dish – the trade mark of centimetres!

Footnote

1. The Grundy Library has since been much enlarged and in consequence occupies a different corner of the building.

Epilogue

By the time of the first anniversary of VE day in May 1946 all of those who had been seconded from industry, universities and other institutions had departed, followed by many others attracted to a wealth of opportunities in other areas. Not least of these was the burgeoning new activity of nuclear energy.

TRE remained with a distinctly 'morning after the night before' feel and indeed before the decade had ended, with the country facing economic strictures, the once vital establishment had reached a low ebb. It would recover. With its integration with ADRDE and later SRDE and its royal title it would in the fullness of time become a recognized centre of excellence.

The TRE of wartime was unique. Never before had there been such a gathering of top scientific and engineering talent under one roof, and it is hardly likely to occur again at a time of national emergency. Science and technology is today a completely different ball game. R & D has become institutionalized. Problems are far more complex, requiring a mainframe computer rather than the back of an envelope for their solution. Upon entering an electronics lab today one is just as likely to see a researcher in front of a VDU as an oscilloscope. His hand will be wielding a 'mouse' or a light-pen rather than a soldering iron. None of these things are much suited to a hut in a muddy field!

And so it was that many of us went our chosen ways, leaving little trace or record of these uniquely British achievements born out of adversity. If little is known of TRE and other wartime experimental establishments beyond those who participated we have only ourselves to blame for even the Official Secrets Act did not preclude one from reporting events and developments in broad terms. Contrast the USA. They wisely (and characteristically) at MIT retained a proportion of staff at the Radiation Laboratory for six months after the cessation of hostilities to record the wartime radar developments. The result was a valuable series of some twenty volumes. Ironically, much of the material therein originated in this country.

There were few honours and awards proffered to scientists and engineers for their war-winning efforts (the phrase 'the boys in the back room' had been coined to describe them – those in the back room are doubtless easily forgotten!); their rewards came mostly from their subsequent peacetime efforts. These have mostly been recorded in the course of my narrative. Many of the principal scientists became Fellows of the Royal Society and of those mentioned in these pages Watson-Watt, Mark Oliphant, John Cockroft, Bernard Lovell, Alan Hodgkin, Martin Ryle, Sam Curran and Group Captain Fennessy were knighted. B.V. Bowden became a life peer. Alan Hodgkin and Martin Ryle both became Nobel Prize winners. The unique honour of having had two future Astronomers Royal working in his division goes to Sidney Jefferson, an original Bawdseyite – they were Professor Martin Ryle and Dr Graham Smith. Perhaps the most significant of the latter-day honours went to Mark Oliphant who was made Governor of South Australia.

From the proceedings of the Royal Commission on Awards to Inventors a number of financial awards were made in the field of radar, not all of which met with universal approval on the part of TRE staff. Watson-Watt devoted his not insignificant sum to setting up Watson-Watt and Partners (his man Wilkins was at least awarded an OBE). Most deserving of these recipients, however, was R.J. Dippy who made a most significant contribution to Bomber Command's eventual success by his invention of GEE.

And what of the man at the helm – A.P. Rowe? There is a certain poignancy about the way he seemed quietly to slip away. Certainly he did not find universal favour but I cannot imagine

TRE would have enjoyed the prominence it did had it not been for his particular if unusual talents. Besides, in civilian life there are no campaign medals, but honours awarded to the chiefs are at least a token to all below him and so it seems TRE's troops went unrecognized. The post of Deputy Controller of Research and Development at the Admiralty to which he acceded was a worthy promotion in itself but no great reward for the man whose concern for the country's defence led to the development of radar, whose perseverance welded together a dissident company of geniuses into a powerhouse of war-winning ideas, to say nothing of the man who established the unique Sunday Soviets – in themselves worth a squadron or two.

It was left to the Americans to recognize his contribution to the Allied victory by awarding him their Medal of Merit. Apart from the award of a CBE in 1942 – the year of the great move (jokers suggested it was for not losing anyone en route for Malvern), 'his own country failed to recognize him as one of the critical agents of survival and victory.' Those were the words in *The Times* obituary in 1976 contributed by Sir Bernard Lovell.

After two years at the Admiralty he departed for Australia to become Vice Chancellor of Adelaide University. While at Adelaide he wrote his book '*One Story of Radar*'. Upon his retirement in 1958 he returned to Malvern and volunteered his services as a part-time teacher at Malvern College. This he did by way of recompense for the college's wartime banishment. He also made the occasional visit to his former empire, but according to a reliable source had a disagreement with the incumbent and was made *persona non grata*.

For a brief period he and his wife went to live in Malta, only to find the climate did not suit his health. They returned to Malvern in the autumn of 1968 where he was to spend his remaining years. Malvern College honoured him in 1972 by making him a governor. His memory and that of TRE is perpetuated by the Rowe room in the science block.

* * *

And so, fifty years after their birth, centimetres and magnetrons are still very much in business. So too are klystrons, finally mastered and useful where the high-power capability of magnetrons is not required. To these two types of microwave generator was later added the 'Travelling Wave Tube.' It was conceived by R. Kampfer, a member of Oliphant's wartime team at Birmingham, but not finally developed until after the war. The unique property of this device is its capability of power amplification.

In this age of semiconductors, thermionic valves are still necessary when high powers for transmitters are required, whatever the frequency. In receivers, however, there have been some spectacular developments in both thermionic and semiconductor devices to achieve high sensitivity and very low noise levels, enabling reception over extreme distances to be achieved.

From its beginnings in the physics laboratory of Birmingham University and a field in Dorset have come a host of devices and services which most of us now take for granted. From the humble domestic microwave oven, air-traffic control, cloud and collision warning radars for airliners, navigational radar for ships both large and small, rain-tracking radar, microwave links for TV and telecommunications, through to the deep probing of space.

There have been many spectacular achievements in man's conquest of space – the moon landings, the tracking of Halley's comet by *Giotto* and the amazing adventures of the *Challenger* probe to name but three. Without centimetre technology none of these voyages into space would have been possible. There is, however, one person who provides a constant link throughout the whole fifty years of these developments – Bernard Lovell, who became a nationally known figure for his pioneering efforts in radio astronomy.

The giant radio telescope, the seeds of which were doubtless sown in those imaginative discussions with which we were entertained during the late-night working sessions of 1940, and the first of its kind in the world, came to fruition in the face of government parsimony and 'those ingrained elephants of inertia' of which Skinner in those words had complained in the early days of centimetre development.

* * *

Of the beginnings of centimetre radar in Dorset there is now virtually no trace. Neither are there ghosts – fresh sea breezes have long exorcised any lingering spirits that may have remained on that ruggedly beautiful St Alban's Head. All that remains to remind one of that momentous summer of 1940 is the little square Norman chapel of St Aldhelm perched high above the sea where it has stood for some 800 years. No one seeing it today would ever guess that it had served as the first-ever target for centimetre radar. Not in our wildest dreams as we toiled to meet the challenge of the German night-bombers did we ever imagine that this entirely new radio technology would one day enable us to view right around the globe by television, or to watch men landing on the moon.

Abbreviations

A III	Assistant Grade III
AA	Anti-aircraft
AC	Alternating Current
ACR	Airfield Control Radar
ADRDE	Air Defence Research & Development Establishment
AFS	Auxiliary Fire Service
AI	Airborne Interception radar
AMRE	Air Ministry Research Establishment
AOC in C	Air Officer Commanding in Chief
ARL	Admiralty Research Laboratories
ASH	American airborne interception radar
ASMI	Airfield Surface Movement Indicator
ASV	Air to Surface Vessel
BBRL	British Based Radiation Laboratory
BK	Barkhausen – Kurz (oscillator)
BN	Blind Navigation (renamed H_2S)
BTH	British Thompson Houston Company
CA & A	Civil Assistant and Accountant
CCE	Controller of Communications Equipment
CD	Coast Defence
CH	Chain Home radar
CHL	Chain Home Low radar
CMH	Centimetre Height-finding
CO	Commanding Officer
DC	Direct Current

DCD	Directorate (or Director) of Communications Development
DOO	Divisional Organizing Officer
DRP	Directorate of Radio Production
DSIR	Department of Scientific and Industrial Research
EU	Engineering Unit
FIU	Fighter Interception Unit
FRS	Fellow of the Royal Society
GCI	Ground Controlled Interception
GEC	General Electric Company
GEE	Code name for airborne navigation system
GI	Government (or General) Issue – US serviceman
GL	Gun-laying
GPO	General Post Office
GRU	Russian military intelligence
H_2S	Radar navigational aid for RAF bombers
HT	High Tension (high voltage)
IFF	Identification Friend or Foe
JSO	Junior Scientific Officer
LA	Laboratory Assistant
LDV	Local Defence Volunteers – original name of Home Guard
LT	Low Tension (low voltage)
MAP	Ministry of Aircraft Production
MAPRE	Ministry of Aircraft Production Research Establishment
MHz	Megahertz
MI5	British Intelligence (home)
MIT	Massachusetts Institute of Technology
PAC	Parachute and Cable
PDS	Post Design Services
PICAO	Provisional International Civil Aviation Organization
PPI	Plan Position Indicator
PO	Petty Officer
RAE	Royal Aircraft Establishment – Farnborough
R & D	Research & Development
RDF	Range and Direction Finding

RPU	Radio Production Unit
RRE	Royal Radar Establishment (formerly TRE)
RSRE	Royal Signals and Radar Establishment
SO	Scientific Officer
SRDE	Signals Research and Development Establishment
STC	Standard Telephones and Cables Company
TFU	Telecommunications Flying Unit
TR (cell)	Transmit & Receive (Switch)
TRE	Telecommunications Research Establishment
VDU	Video Display Unit
VE	Victory in Europe
WAAF	Women's Auxiliary Air Force
WD	War Department
WVS	Women's Voluntary Service

Bibliography

Bowen, E.G., *Radar Days* (Adam Hilger, 1987)

IEE Proceedings (special issue) *'Historical Radar'* (Vol. 132, Pt. A, No. 6, October 1985)

Johnson, Brian, *The Secret War* (BBC Publications, 1978)

Jones, R.V., *Most Secret War* (Coronet Books, 5th impression, 1985)

Kinsey, Gordon, *Bawdsey* (Terence Dalton Ltd, 1983)

Rowe, A.P., *One Story of Radar* (Cambridge University Press, 1948)

Saward, Dudley, *Bernard Lovell* (Robert Hale, 1984)

Index